# SADLIER PHONICS

W9-CUE-274

## Level B

### Lesley Mandel Morrow
### Senior Author

### Marie Garman    Patricia Maureen Mount    Patricia Scanlon

## Literacy Consultants

**Heather K. Casey, Ph.D.**
Department of Teacher Education
Rider University

**Ernest Morrell, Ph.D.**
Graduate School of Education
University of California, Los Angeles

**Jennifer Rowsell, Ph.D.**
Graduate School of Education
Rutgers University

**Erica C. Boling, Ph.D.**
Graduate School of Education
Rutgers University

**Robert Calfee, Ph.D.**
Graduate School of Education
University of California, Riverside

**Robert Rueda, Ph.D.**
Rossier School of Education
University of Southern California

**Carmelita Williams, Ed.D.**
Graduate School of Education
Norfolk State University

**Cheryl Dyer**
Assistant Superintendent
Bridgewater-Raritan (NJ) School District

**Eleanor M. Vargas**
Teacher Education Department
Claremont Graduate University

**Diane H. Tracey, Ed.D.**
College of Education
Kean University

**D. Ray Reutzel, Ph.D.**
Emma Eccles Jones College of Education
and Human Services
Utah State University

Printed in the United States of America.          ISBN: 978-0-8215-7902-2          18 19 20 21 22 SHNW 26 25 24 23 22

# Contents

**Unit 4 continued on next pa**

☆ **Essential Skill**

## Syllables, Compound Words, y as a Vowel, Consonant Digraphs, Silent Letters, and r-Controlled Vowels
### Theme: Going Places

## Vowel Digraphs and Diphthongs
### Theme: A Rainbow of Colors

☆ **Essential Skill**

★ **Essential Skill**

# A Friend

It's fun to have a friend!
Someone to see and stay with
To walk and talk and play with
To laugh and shout HURRAY with
It's fun to have a friend!

We might not even talk!
We might just sit and giggle
Until we wiggle-wiggle
Or leap and jump and jiggle
We might not even talk!

It's fun to have a friend!
To hold a hand and go with
To ask and learn and know with
To sing and dance and grow with
It's fun to have a friend!

*Betsy Jones Michael*

**Critical Thinking**   Why is it fun to have a friend?
How can you make new friends?

Name _____

# Dear Family,

**A**s your child progresses through this unit about friendship, he or she will review the sounds of the consonants. The 21 letters of the alphabet that are consonants are shown below.

- Point to each consonant and have your child say its name.

# Apreciada Familia,

**E**n esta unidad, acerca de la amistad, su niño repasará los sonidos de las consonantes. Las siguientes letras son las 21 consonantes del idioma inglés.

- Señale cada consonante y pida al niño que diga el nombre.

- Read the poem "A Friend" on the reverse side. Talk about things friends do together.

- Read the poem again. Ask your child to say the first and last lines of each stanza with you.

- Help your child identify some of the consonants in the poem. Ask what sounds they make.

- Lea al niño la poesía "A Friend" en la página 5. Converse con su niño acerca de lo que hacen los amigos cuando están juntos.

- Lea el poema de nuevo. Pida a su hijo recitar con usted los dos primeros versos de cada estrofa.

- Repasen las consonantes que aparecen en la poesía. ¿Cómo suenan?

## PROJECT

**A**sk your child to name some of his or her friends. Together, make a list of the names. Underline single consonants in each name. Then have your child choose one friend and write, call, or draw him or her.

Carmela
Omar
Lisa
Jason
Karen

## PROYECTO

**P**ida a su niño nombrar a algunos de sus amigos. Después escriban los nombres. Subrayen las consonantes en cada nombre. Luego pídale que escriba una carta, llame, o dibuje a uno de sus amigos.

 Visit us at **www.sadlierphonicsonline.com**

Name _____

**Pals** begins with the sound of **p. Listen** for beginning consonant sounds in the rhyme.

We're best pals,
so meet me at noon
to take a fun ride
in a hot-air balloon.

**Here's a Hint!**
The letters **b, c, d, f, g, h, j, k, l, m, n, p, q, r, s, t, v, w, x, y,** and **z** are consonants.

**Say** the name of the picture. **Write** the letter or letters that stand for the beginning consonant sound.

| j | m | k | f | z | y | r | b | qu | h | w | p |
|---|---|---|---|---|---|---|---|----|----|----|----|

| | |
|---|---|
| **1.** | **2.** |
| **3.** | **4.** |

| **5.** | **6.** |
|---|---|
| **7.** | **8.** |

| **9.** | **10.** |
|---|---|
| **11.** | **12.** |

**Great** ends with the sound of **t**.
**Listen** for ending consonant sounds in the rhyme.

You're great. You're fun.
I like you, bud.
I like you better
than a pig likes mud.

 **Say** the name of the picture. **Circle** the letter that stands for the ending consonant sound.

| | | |
|---|---|---|
| **1.**    b   d   t | **2.**    p   m   g | **3.**    l   b   g |
| **4.**    f   s   l | **5.**    l   m   j | **6.**    t   d   n |
| **7.**    k   h   f | **8.**    m   c   n | **9.**    z   t   d |
| **10.**    t   p   z | **11.**    h   s   n | **12.**    w   f   k |
| **13.**    d   f   k | **14.**    t   x   d | **15.**    f   l   d |

**Lesson 3** • Connecting Sound to Symbol:
Final Consonants

**PHONICS ALIVE AT HOME** Say **b** and ask your child to point to a picture that ends with **b** and say its name. Repeat with other final consonants.

Name _____

**Shadow** has the sound of **d** in the middle.
**Listen** for middle consonant sounds in the rhyme.

My buddy Shadow
follows me all day.
But when the sunny day is gone,
she cannot stay and play.

**Say** the name of each picture. **Draw** a line from the picture to the letter or letters that stand for the middle consonant sound.

1.   ●          ● v

2. 7   ●          ● m

3.   ●          ● b

4.   ●          ● c

5.   ●          ● t

6.   ●          ● l

7.   ●          ● ll

8.   ●          ● tt

9.   ●          ● g

10.   ●          ● n

11.   ●          ● pp

12.   ●          ● mm

**Review**

**Look** at the picture clues. **Fill in** the missing letters in the puzzles.

**ACROSS**

1. 

3. 

**DOWN**

1. 

2. 

**ACROSS**

4. 7

5. 

6. 

**DOWN**

4. 

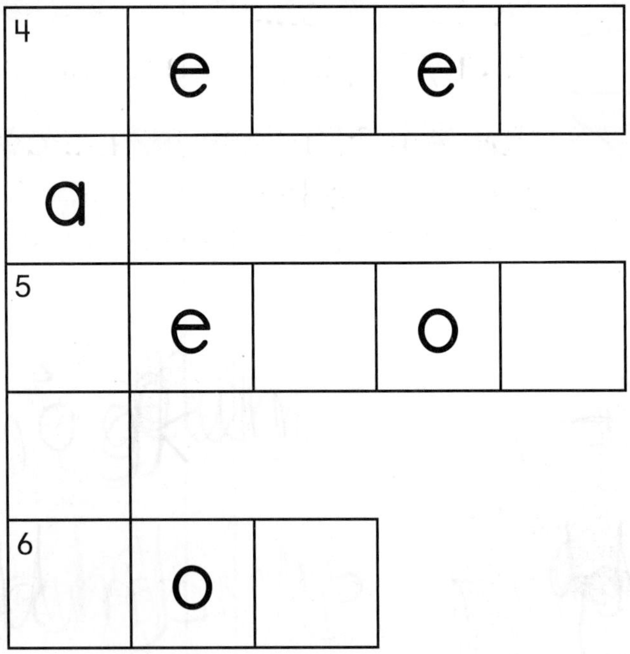


**Write on Track**

What seven things could you and your friend put in a backpack? Name each thing and write the letters that stand for the beginning and ending consonant sounds.

PHONICS ALIVE AT HOME

With your child, look at a grocery list you have at home. Point to a word and have your child name the initial, final, and middle consonants.

**READ**

Read the page. Talk about friendship.

## Learn About Friendship

We're best **buddies** in English.
In Spanish, we're **amigos.**
Speak French and call us **amis.**
I'll speak Swahili and call you **rafiki.**
You speak Japanese and call
me **tomodachi.**
In any language, we're friends.

How are friends the same all
over the world?

**Check-Up** Say the name of the picture. Write the letter that stands for the missing sound. Then trace the whole word.

**1.**

_____ o g

**2.**

_____ a m

**3.**

_____ a r n

**4.**

_____ f o

**5.**

_____ m a

**6.**

_____ h o o

**7.**

s a _ a d

**8.**

_ l e _ o n

**9.**

r o _ o t

**10.**

_____ o p

**11.**

w a _ e r

**12.**

_____ p e

PHONICS ALIVE AT HOME

Review this Check-Up with your child.

# Friends of Mine

1

**Reading at Home:** Read the book with your child. Talk about what the friends do together in the story. Then have your child identify consonant sounds in words in the story.

Fold

3

Jan is my pen pal.
We write letters to each other.

Fold

Think about your best friend and what you like to do together. Then draw a picture.

8

Kareem is my buddy.
We ride bikes together on Saturdays.

9

Read the page. Talk about Niagara Falls.

## Learn About Niagara Falls

Welcome to Niagara Falls. These falls are in New York and in Canada. Do you want to see the top? Visit the tower on the New York side. Watch the water rush right down with a crash.

Would you like a closer look? Put on a raincoat and ride around on the boat called *Maid of the Mist*. But don't get upset if you get wet!

What else would you like to know about Niagara Falls?

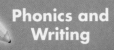

# Why Swim?

Do you think it's important to know how to swim? **Answer** the question and give your reasons. Use one or more words from the box.

**Writer's Tips**
- Clearly state your point of view.
- Give specific reasons why you think the way you do.

| swim | laps | wet | jump | not |
|------|------|-----|------|-----|
| drip | fast | best | run | flop |

I think _____

_____

Reason #1 _____

_____

_____

Reason #2 _____

_____

_____

PHONICS ALIVE AT HOME

Have your child circle all the short vowel words he or she wrote. Then have your child write a li of words that rhyme with the words in the box.

Name _____

Check-Up

**Say** the name of the picture. **Fill in** the circle next to the word that names it.

**1.**
- ○ fun
- ○ fan
- ○ fin

**2.**
- ○ big
- ○ bag
- ○ bug

**3.**
- ○ pig
- ○ pug
- ○ peg

**4.**
- ○ leg
- ○ lag
- ○ log

**5.**
- ○ bud
- ○ bed
- ○ bid

**6.**
- ○ not
- ○ nut
- ○ net

**7.**
eggs
bread
milk
juice
apples
- ○ list
- ○ lost
- ○ last

**8.**
- ○ hum
- ○ him
- ○ ham

**9.**
- ○ wall
- ○ will
- ○ well

**10.**
- ○ cab
- ○ cub
- ○ cob

**11.**
- ○ led
- ○ lad
- ○ lid

**12.**
- ○ sock
- ○ sick
- ○ sack

**13.**
- ○ pin
- ○ pan
- ○ pet

**14.**
- ○ cap
- ○ cot
- ○ cat

**15.**
- ○ hit
- ○ hut
- ○ hat

# Assessment

**Check-Up** **Say** the name of the picture. **Write** its name on the line.

| | | |
|---|---|---|
| 1. | 2. | 3. |
| 4. | 5. | 6. |
| 7. | 8. | 9. |
| 10. | 11. | 12. |
| 13. | 14. | 15. |

**40**

**Lesson 22** • Assessing Short Vowels

PHONICS
ALIVE AT HOME

Point to a picture. Have your child tell you its name. Then ask your child to name other words with the same short vowel sound.

Name _____

# Water's Song

**Reading at Home:** Read the book with your child. Talk about the different things that water can do. Then have your child identify the short vowel sounds in the rhyming words.

—Fold—

1

✂

water lapping on the sand.

3

—Fold—

Seas carrying giant ships taking people on long trips.

8

✂

Oceans sending pretty shells,

9

4

Raindrops falling on city blocks,

Fold

2

Rivers cutting through the land,

Fold

5

waves crashing around the rocks.

7

water pumped from farmers' wells.

# TREES

Trees are the kindest things I know,
They do no harm, they simply grow

And spread a shade for sleepy cows,
And gather birds among their boughs.

They give us fruit in leaves above,
And wood to make our houses of,

And leaves to burn on Hallowe'en,
And in the Spring new buds of green.

They are the first when day's begun
To touch the beams of morning sun,

They are the last to hold the light
When evening changes into night,

And when a moon floats on the sky
They hum a drowsy lullaby

Of sleepy children long ago…
Trees are the kindest things I know.

*Harry Behn*

**Critical Thinking**  In what other ways are trees kind?
What can you do to be kind to trees?

Name _____

# Dear Family,

**A**s your child progresses through this unit about trees and nature, he or she will review the long vowel sounds of **a**, **i**, **o**, **u**, and **e**.

• Say the picture names together and listen to the long vowel sounds. Long vowels say their own names.

# Apreciada Familia,

**E**n esta unidad, acerca de la naturaleza, su niño repasará los sonidos largos de las vocales **a, i, o, u, e.**

• Pronuncien el nombre de las cosas y escuchen el sonido largo de las vocales. El sonido largo es como el nombre de la vocal.

| a | i | o | u | e |
|---|---|---|---|---|
|  |  |  |  |  |
| **rain** | **vine** | **rose** | **fruit** | **read** |

• Read the poem "Trees" on the reverse side. Talk about ways that trees help us.

• Ask your child to find the rhyming words at the end of each pair of lines, for example: **know** and **grow**.

• Help your child find some of the long vowel words in the poem. (**trees**, **know**, **grow**, **shade**, **sleepy**, **fruit**, **leaves**, **make**, **green**, **beams**, **floats**)

• Lea la poesía "Trees" en la página 43. Hablen sobre cómo los árboles nos ayudan.

• Pida al niño encontrar la palabra que rima al final de cada par de versos, por ejemplo: **know** y **grow**.

• Ayude al niño a encontrar algunas palabras donde el sonido de la vocal es largo. (**trees**, **know**, **grow**, **shade**, **sleepy**, **fruit**, **leaves**, **make**, **green**, **beams**, **floats**)

## PROJECT

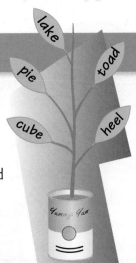

**H**elp your child make a word tree from a small branch that has fallen off a tree. Place the branch in a can filled with dirt or clay. Then have your child draw leaves and cut them out. He or she can write new long vowel words on the leaves and attach them to the tree.

## PROYECTO

**H**aga un árbol de palabras. Recojan una ramita caída y pónganla en una lata llena de tierra o barro. Haga que el niño dibuje hojas y las recorte. A medida que el niño vaya aprendiendo palabras donde el sonido de las vocales es largo, puede escribirlas en las hojas y atarlas al árbol.

Visit us at **www.sadlierphonicsonline.com**

Name __Elena__

**Work Together**

Work with a partner to complete each sentence by choosing the long **a** or long **i** words that make sense. One partner can write the first word, and the other partner can write the second word.

**1.** CAMP PINE TREE

Pain    (Pine)    (like)

We ___like___ Camp ___Pine___ Tree.

**2.**

ride    pale    bikes

We _____ our _____ up a hill.

**3.**

day    pie    hike

We _____ all _____ long.

**4.**

high    way    dive

We fly a kite _____ up _____.

**5.**

save    lie    bright

We _____ under _____ stars.

**6.**

say    night    time

It's time to _____ good _____.

**Read** the poem. **Underline** the long **a** and long **i** words. Then **number** the sentences in order to tell what to do.

# Time to Dine

Make a fine bird feeder,
tie it tightly with twine,
and hang it way up high
from a wide, tall tree.

Now hide and stay quite still.
For in a little while,
the birds will come to dine.
Just wait and you will see!

_____ Hang the feeder up high.

_____ Make a fine bird feeder.

_____ Hide so the birds don't see you.

_____ Tie twine to the bird feeder.

Lesson 28 • Long Vowels **a** and **i** in Context
Comprehension: Identifying Steps in a Process

PHONICS
ALIVE AT HOME

Talk about the poem. Ask your child to tell what to do first, second, third, and last if you want to see lots of birds.

Name _____

**Leaves** has the long **e** sound. **Listen** for the sound of long **e** in the rhyme.

I see beech leaves.
Let's put them in a heap.
Sweep them up neatly,
then take a giant leap!

 The letters **ee** and **ea** stand for long **e. Say** the name of the picture. If its name has the long **e** sound, write **ee** or **ea.** Then **trace** the whole word.

**Here's a Hint!**
If there are two vowels in a one-syllable word, the first vowel is usually **long** and the second vowel is silent. There are different ways to spell long **e.**

|  | b<u>ee</u> | | 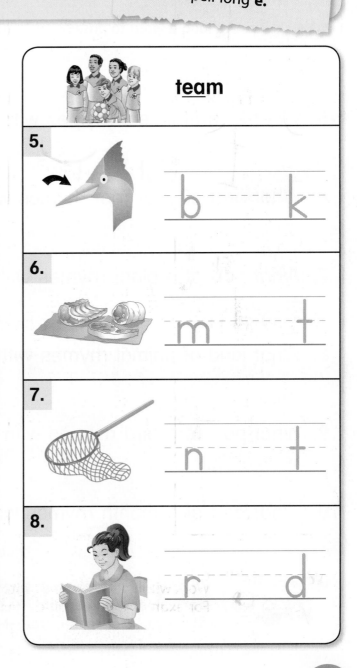 | t<u>ea</u>m |
|---|---|---|---|---|
| **1.** | s ___ d | | **5.** | b ___ k |
| **2.** | b ___ d | | **6.** | m ___ t |
| **3.** | qu ___ n | | **7.** | n ___ t |
| **4.** | tr ___ | | **8.** | r ___ d |

**Long e Word Families**

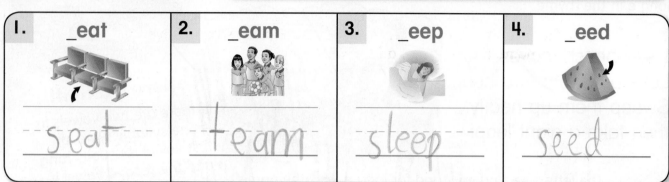

Say the phonogram. Say the name of the picture and write the word.

| 1. _eat | 2. _eam | 3. _eep | 4. _eed |
|---------|---------|---------|---------|
|  seat | team | sleep | seed |

Write a long **e** word to answer each question.

5. What kind of insect rhymes with **see?**

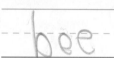
bee

6. What part of your foot rhymes with **feel?**

heel

7. What part of a plant rhymes with **reed?**

need

8. What kind of animal rhymes with **real?**

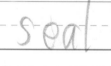
seal

9. What part of a bird rhymes with **leak?**

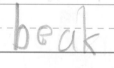
beak

10. What part of a month rhymes with **peek?**

week

**Write on Track**  Write a silly question that begins "Have you ever seen . . . ?"
Use as many long **e** words as possible. For example,
"Have you ever **seen** a **tree** of **green beans**?"

**PHONICS ALIVE AT HOME**  Take turns with your child asking and answering the questions on the page.

Name _____

Long o, u, e

**Work Together** **Fill in** the circle next to the word that completes the sentence. **Write** the word in the sentence. Then **read** the sentences and have a partner name the long **o, u,** and **e** words.

1. You can _____ a lot in a tree.

○ see
○ seal

2. Let's take a _____.

○ neat
○ peek

3. The baby birds' nest is their _____.

○ home
○ hose

4. A mother bird has food in her _____.

○ bead
○ beak

5. Aren't the baby birds _____?

○ cute
○ clue

6. Each bug has its _____ leaf.

○ road
○ own

7. Squirrels _____ nuts.

○ meet
○ eat

Read the poem. Underline the long **o, u,** and **e** words. Write long **o, u,** or **e** words to complete the sentences.

The Clean Team

Call the Clean Team
and ask for Duke or Dee.
We're the ones to make your yard
as neat as yards can be.

We'll rake up all the leaves that fall
from each and every tree.
We hope that you'll be glad to know—
we do it all for free.

1. Call the _____ Team.

2. Ask for _____ or Dee.

3. The Clean Team will rake up _____.

4. The Clean Team works for _____.

PHONICS ALIVE AT HOME

Talk about the poem with you child. Ask: What is this poem all about?

Read and Write   Read the story. Then answer the questions.

## Johnny Appleseed

Johnny Appleseed lived a long time ago. Do you know the good things that he did?

Johnny wanted apple trees to grow all over America. So as a young man, Johnny left his home. He walked across the land planting apple trees.

Johnny was nice to people. He gave them apple seeds and trees to plant. He did not make poor people pay for them. He wanted them to have fruit to eat.

Years later, Johnny returned to the places he had been. He was proud to see apple trees growing there. Apple trees may still be there today!

1. What was one way Johnny Appleseed was nice to people?

_____

_ _ _ _ _ _ _ _ _ _ _ _ _ _ _ _ _ _ _ _ _ _ _ _ _ _ _

_____

2. How can you be like Johnny Appleseed?

_____

_ _ _ _ _ _ _ _ _ _ _ _ _ _ _ _ _ _ _ _ _ _ _ _ _ _ _

_____

## Review

Combine words from boxes 1, 2, and 3 to **write** sentences. How many different sentences can you write?

| 1. | 2. | 3. |
|---|---|---|
| Jolly Jane<br>Queen Jean<br>Mr. Mike | plays the flute<br>rides a goat<br>plants a tree | on a dune.<br>each May.<br>on the road. |

**64**  Lesson 35 • Reviewing Long Vowels

Name _____

**Spell, Write, and Tell** Say, spell, and talk about each word in the box. Write each word under the long vowel sound in its name.

| coat |
| eat |
| five |
| fruit |
| home |
| make |
| may |
| pie |
| tree |
| tune |

**1.** Long **a**
_____
_____
_____
_____

**2.** Long **i**
_____
_____
_____
_____

**3.** Long **o**
_____
_____
_____
_____

**4.** Long **u**
_____
_____
_____
_____

**5.** Long **e**
_____
_____
_____
_____

## Spelling and Writing

**Spell, Write, and Tell** Make a list of things to do as you sit under an apple tree. Use two or more of the words in the box. **Share** your favorite things with the class.

| | | | | |
|---|---|---|---|---|
| coat | eat | five | fruit | home |
| make | may | pie | tree | tune |

## Things To Do

hum a tune

make five frui

I eat pie

go Home

hit the tree

PHONICS ALIVE AT HOME  Ask your child to read the items on the list and point out the spelling words he or she used.

Name _____

**READ** Read the page. **Talk** about a tree named General Sherman.

## Learn About Giant Trees

Did you know that one of the biggest trees in the world is in a national park in California? Its name is General Sherman. General Sherman's trunk is very, very wide. It would take about 25 children holding hands to make a circle around this huge tree. General Sherman is also very tall. The next time you're in a city, look up at a high building and count 26 floors. That's how tall General Sherman is.

So if you ever go to Sequoia National Park, stop in to see the General. You'll get a BIG thrill!

GENERAL SHERMAN

# Dear Gardener...

**Writer's Tips**
• A thank-you letter tells someone how you feel about what he or she did for you or gave you.
• A letter includes the date (the heading), a greeting (Dear…), what you want to say (the body), the closing (Yours truly), and your name.

Trees give us shade, fruit, and clean air. **Write** a thank-you letter to the person who planted your favorite tree. Say why you're glad your favorite tree exists.

| shade | light | oak | leaves | juice |
|-------|-------|-----|--------|-------|
| day | smile | hope | seeds | fruit |

Date: _____

Dear Gardener,

_____

_____

_____

_____

_____

_____

Yours truly,

_____

_____

**PHONICS ALIVE AT HOME** Ask your child to read the letter alou Then help your child underline all of the long vowel words.

Name _____

**Check-Up**

Say the name of the picture. Write its name on the line.

| | | |
|---|---|---|
| 1. | 2. | 3. |
| 4. | 5. | 6. |
| 7. | 8. | 9. |
| 10. | 11. | 12. |
| 13. | 14. | 15. |

Check-Up
**Say** the name of the picture. **Fill in** the circle next to the word that names it.

**1.**
- ○ van
- ○ vane
- ○ vine

**2.**
- ○ glue
- ○ clue
- ○ glum

**3.**
- ○ hat
- ○ hay
- ○ high

**4.**
- ○ raid
- ○ read
- ○ road

**5.**
- ○ rope
- ○ slow
- ○ row

**6.**
- ○ tube
- ○ tub
- ○ tune

**7.**
- ○ lack
- ○ late
- ○ lake

**8.**
- ○ pine
- ○ pie
- ○ pane

**9.**
- ○ tone
- ○ tied
- ○ toad

Check-Up
**Underline** all the words that have a long vowel sound. Then **circle** **Yes** or **No** to answer each question.

| | | |
|---|---|---|
| **10.** Does a bee sleep in a bed? | Yes | No |
| **11.** Can a goat paint a gate? | Yes | No |
| **12.** Can a seal swim in the sea? | Yes | No |
| **13.** Is a peach a fruit? | Yes | No |
| **14.** Is a cape a big cap? | Yes | No |
| **15.** Can you hide a flute in a lime? | Yes | No |
| **16.** Is a dime the same as a vine? | Yes | No |
| **17.** Can you eat ice cream in a cone? | Yes | No |

PHONICS ALIVE AT HOME
Review this Check-U with your child.

Name _____

Leaves and Seeds

— Fold —

Reading at Home: Read the book with your child to find out about different kinds of leaves and seeds. Have your child find words with long vowels, such as **trees, oak, pine, blue,** and **name.**

Pine trees and blue spruce have needles for leaves. They keep their leaves all year.

— Fold —

Draw a picture of a leaf or a seed. Write its name.

8

Some seeds are inside fruit. Can you describe the seed of an apple, an orange, a lime, or a peach?

6

**DIRECTIONS:** Cut and fold the book.

2

There are many different trees. Each kind of tree has a different leaf.

oak leaf

pine needles

maple leaf

— Fold —

4

Some trees, like oaks and maples, lose their leaves in the fall. New leaves grow back in the spring.

— Fold —

7

Some seeds are nuts. Walnuts, pecans, almonds, and Brazil nuts are all seeds.

almond

walnut

Brazil nut

pecan

5

Trees grow from seeds.

oak

maple

elm

# CITY STREET

Honk—honk—honk!
Beep—beep—beep!
Hear the noise
Of city street.

Cars race fast,
Trucks bump past;
Creeping slow
The buses go.

Green turns red,
A sudden stop;
Up the hand
Of traffic cop.

Whistle shrill—
All is still;
Sudden hush—
The people rush.

Red turns green,
Then on again;
Cars race fast,
Trucks bump past.

*Lois Lenski*

**Critical Thinking** How is the place where you live like this busy city?
How is it different?

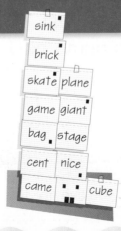

# PHONICS ALIVE AT HOME

Name _____

## Dear Family,

**A**s your child progresses through this unit about cities, she or he will learn about the two sounds of **c** and **g** and about consonant blends. A **consonant blend** is two or three consonants sounded together in a word so that each letter is heard.

- Read the words below with your child. Listen to the sounds of the letters that are underlined.

| Hard c | Soft c |
|--------|--------|
| <u>c</u>ar | <u>c</u>ity |

| Hard g | Soft g |
|--------|--------|
| <u>g</u>o | <u>g</u>ym |

| Consonant Blends | |
|--------|--------|
| <u>pl</u>ay | re<u>nt</u> |

- Read the poem "City Street" on the reverse side. Talk about the city scene.

- Help your child find words in the poem that sound like what they mean, for example: **honk, beep, bump.**

- Point out the consonant sounds in these words from the poem: soft **c** (<u>c</u>ity, ra<u>c</u>e); hard **c** (<u>c</u>ars, <u>c</u>op); hard **g** (<u>g</u>o); consonant blends (ho<u>nk</u>, <u>str</u>eet, fa<u>st</u>, <u>tr</u>ucks, bu<u>mp</u>, <u>cr</u>eeping, <u>sl</u>ow, <u>gr</u>een, <u>st</u>op, ha<u>nd</u>, <u>tr</u>affic).

## Apreciada Familia,

**E**n esta unidad, sobre las ciudades, su niño aprenderá los dos sonidos de las letras **c** y **g** y la combinación de sonidos de las consonantes. Una **combinación de sonidos** se forma cuando dos o más consonantes están juntas pero cada una tiene su propio sonido al pronunciar la palabra.

- Lean las siguientes palabras. Escuchen el sonido de las letras subrayadas.

- Lean la poesía "City Street" en la página 75. Hablen de la escena en la ciudad.

- Ayude al niño a encontrar palabras cuyo sonido se parezca a su significado, por ejemplo: **honk, beep, bump.**

- Señale los sonidos de las consonantes en estas palabras de la poesía: **c** suave (<u>c</u>ity, ra<u>c</u>e); **c** fuerte (<u>c</u>ars, <u>c</u>op); **g** fuerte (<u>g</u>o); combinación de consonantes (ho<u>nk</u>, <u>str</u>eet, fa<u>st</u>, <u>tr</u>ucks, bu<u>mp</u>, <u>cr</u>eeping, <u>sl</u>ow, <u>gr</u>een, <u>st</u>op, ha<u>nd</u>, <u>tr</u>affic).

## PROJECT

**M**ake a city skyscraper with your child. Use index cards or pieces of paper for the bricks. When your child learns a new word with hard or soft **c** or **g** or with a consonant blend, have him or her write the word on a brick and add it to the building.

## PROYECTO

**H**agan juntos un rascacielos. Usen tarjetas de 3X5 o pedazos de papel para los ladrillos. Cuando el niño aprenda una palabra nueva con sonido suave o fuerte de la **c** o la **g,** o de combinación, pídale que la escriba en un ladrillo y la pegue al edificio.

Name _____

**Block** begins with the l blend **bl.**
**Listen** for the sounds of l blends in the rhyme.

My block has a clock
plus a flag and a slide.
Please come to my block.
We'll play and we'll glide.

**Say** the name of the picture. **Circle** the l blend that begins its name.

**Here's a Hint!**
A **consonant blend** is two or three consonants sounded together in a word so that each letter is heard.

1.
gl
pl
sl

2.
gl
pl
fl

3.
sl
pl
bl

4.
bl
cl
fl

5.
cl
fl
sl

6.
sl
gl
bl

7.
bl
cl
gl

8.
bl
sl
pl

9.
bl
cl
pl

10.
pl
sl
fl

11.
bl
cl
gl

12.
fl
gl
bl

**Write on Track**
Write a sentence about something you see on a city block. Use a word with an l blend. For example, "I see a bank with two big **clocks**."

**Crews** begins with the **r** blend **cr.**
**Listen** for the sounds of **r** blends in the rhyme.

Crews, fix the freeway!
Trucks, bring the gravel!
Now press quickly!
Drivers want to travel!

**Here's a Hint!**
A **consonant blend** is two or three consonants sounded together in a word so that each letter is heard.

 **Say** the name of the picture. **Add** an **r** blend to **write** the picture name. Then **trace** the whole word.

| br | cr | dr | fr | gr | pr | tr |
|----|----|----|----|----|----|----|

| 1. | 2. | 3. | 4. |
|----|----|----|----|
| ___ ain | ___ um | ___ ow | ___ ick |

| 5. | 6. | 7. | 8. |
|----|----|----|----|
| ___ een | ___ ize | ___ ame | ___ ill |

| 9. | 10. | 11. | 12. |
|----|----|----|----|
| ___ ee | ___ ide | ___ og | ___ awl |

**PHONICS ALIVE AT HOME**
With your child, take turns saying words that begin with **br, cr, dr, fr, gr, pr,** or **tr.**

Name _____

**Swing** begins with the **s** blend **sw.**
**Listen** for the sounds of **s** blends in the rhyme.

We play baseball on my street.
Swing that bat.
Smack that ball.
Now start running. Move those feet!

**Here's a Hint!**
A **consonant blend** is two or three consonants sounded together in a word so that each letter is heard.

**Say** the name of each picture. **Circle** the picture if its name begins with the same **s** blend as the first picture in the row. **Write** the blend.

| | | | | |
|---|---|---|---|---|
| **I.** |  **st**amp |  |  | ★ |
| **2.** | **sw**im | | | |
| **3.** | **sp**ill | | | |
| **4.** | **sk**ate | | | |

Read the name of the picture. Write a word with the same phonogram. Begin the new word with an **l** blend, **r** blend, or **s** blend from the box.

| cl | sl | cr | tr | st | spr |
|----|----|----|----|----|-----|

**1.**

rock

_____

- - - - - - - - - -

_____

**2.**

head

_____

- - - - - - - - - -

_____

**3.**

bean

_____

- - - - - - - - - -

_____

**4.**

kick

_____

- - - - - - - - - -

_____

**5.**

ride

_____

- - - - - - - - - -

_____

**6.**

bow

_____

- - - - - - - - - -

_____

Circle and write a blend to complete the word in each sentence.

**7.** Greg's house is made of _____**ick.**          cr     br     dr

**8.** Sue raised the _____**ag** to start the race.     sl     gl     fl

**9.** Dad piled his _____**ate** with food.          pl     bl     cl

**10.** Jen tied _____**ing** to the kite.          spr     scr     str

PHONICS ALIVE AT HOME — With your child, think of rhyming words that begin with the same blends as words in items 7–10, such as **brick/trick.**

Name _____

**Lift** ends with the consonant blend **ft. Listen** for the sounds of the final consonant blends in the rhyme.

Lift the last plank.
Don't let it bump or tilt!
Hold it still. I'll bolt it.
Now look what we have built!

**Here's a Hint!**
A **consonant blend** is two or three consonants sounded together in a word so that each letter is heard.

**Say** the name of the picture. **Circle** the blend that ends its name.

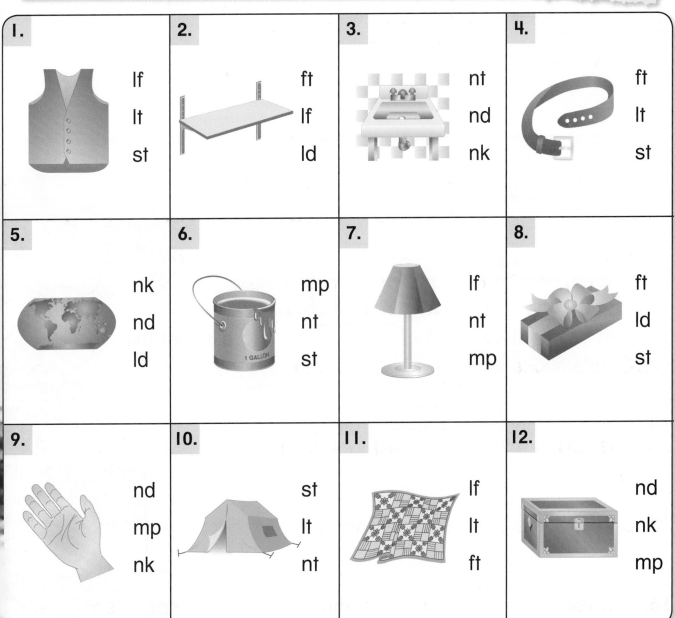

| | | | |
|---|---|---|---|
| 1. lf lt st | 2. ft lf ld | 3. nt nd nk | 4. ft lt st |
| 5. nk nd ld | 6. mp nt st | 7. lf nt mp | 8. ft ld st |
| 9. nd mp nk | 10. st lt nt | 11. lf lt ft | 12. nd nk mp |

# Final Blends

**Read** each word. **Write** a word with the same final blend.

| | | | |
|---|---|---|---|
| **1.** ve**st** | **2.** bu**mp** | **3.** me**lt** | **4.** li**ft** |
| **5.** co**ld** | **6.** we**nt** | **7.** be**nd** | **8.** bu**nk** |
| **9.** sta**mp** | **10.** dri**nk** | **11.** sta**nd** | **12.** twi**st** |

---

Use a word from the box to complete each sentence.

| stand | went | best | drink |
|---|---|---|---|

**13.** Last week, Mom and I _____ to a street fair.

**14.** First we stopped at a fresh fruit _____ .

**15.** Then we got grape juice to _____ .

**16.** We had the _____ time together!

FRESH FRUIT

PHONICS ALIVE AT HOME

Ask your child to read each word he or she wrote and circle the final blen (the last two letters).

Name _____

**Read** the letter. **Answer** the questions.

Dear Grandpa,

Today we drove to see the cliffs in Colorado. Long ago, Native Americans made their homes in the cliffs. One huge cliff house is called Cliff Palace. Up to 400 people lived there! It had over 200 rooms. That's more than in my apartment building.

My building has four floors. Parts of Cliff Palace also have four floors. But I use stairs to climb up and down the floors. The people in Cliff Palace used ladders.

I'm glad we went to Cliff Palace. But I still like my apartment building the best!

Love and hugs,

Gail

1. What is one way Cliff Palace is the same as an apartment building?

_____

_____

2. What is one way Cliff Palace is different than an apartment building?

_____

_____

 Say the name of the picture and **read** the word. **Change** the blend to **write** the word that names the picture.

**1.**

pride

_____

_ _ _ _ _ _ _ _ _ _ _ _

_____

**2.**

spill

_____

_ _ _ _ _ _ _ _ _ _ _ _

_____

**3.**

snow

_____

_ _ _ _ _ _ _ _ _ _ _ _

_____

**4.**

bring

_____

_ _ _ _ _ _ _ _ _ _ _ _

_____

**5.**

trim

_____

_ _ _ _ _ _ _ _ _ _ _ _

_____

**6.**

scat

_____

_ _ _ _ _ _ _ _ _ _ _ _

_____

**7.**

bend

_____

_ _ _ _ _ _ _ _ _ _ _ _

_____

**8.**

bank

_____

_ _ _ _ _ _ _ _ _ _ _ _

_____

**9.**

test

_____

_ _ _ _ _ _ _ _ _ _ _ _

_____

**10.**

wind

_____

_ _ _ _ _ _ _ _ _ _ _ _

_____

**11.**

land

_____

_ _ _ _ _ _ _ _ _ _ _ _

_____

**12.**

lift

_____

_ _ _ _ _ _ _ _ _ _ _ _

_____

PHONICS ALIVE AT HOME — Ask your child to read a word he or she wrote and then say a word that begins o ends with the same two letters.

Name _____

**Spell, Write, and Tell**

Say, spell, and talk about each word in the box. Write each word under the blend in its name.

| train | glue | jump | flag | space | green | help | stage | play | fast | from | squeak |

**1.** **l** Blend

**2.** **r** Blend

**3.** **s** Blend

**4.** Final Blend

Spell, Write, and Tell

**Write** what you might see and hear at a play called "City Streets." Use words from the box. **Read** your description to the class.

| | | | | | |
|---|---|---|---|---|---|
| train | glue | jump | flag | space | green |
| help | stage | play | fast | from | squeak |

## CiTY STREETS

Scenery: What You Will See

Sound Effects: What You Will Hear

**Lesson 52** • Connecting Spelling, Writing, and Speaking

PHONICS ALIVE AT HOME

With your child, write sentences about your neighborhood using some of the words in the box.

Name _____

# City Beat

— 1

Reading at Home: After reading the book with your child, ask if the city is "the best." Why or why not? Together, find a word that begins with a consonant blend, and a word with a soft c or soft g.

Fold

Cars and trucks are slow or fast, blocks of people move right past. Slow—fast—move right past.

A & C CARPETS

TAXI

109

3

Fold

Uptown, downtown, children say, it's the place to work and play. Uptown—downtown—work and play.

8

Lights are blinking, high and low, red means stop, green means go. Red—green—stop and go.

WALK

ONE WAY

3RD AVE MAIN ST

9

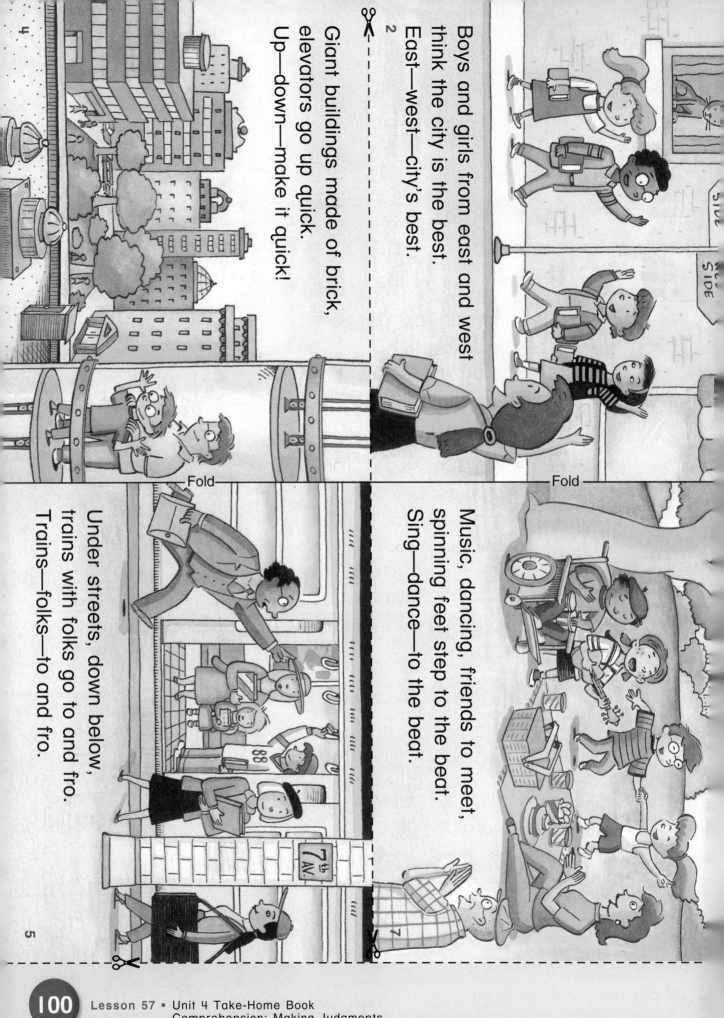

Boys and girls from east and west
think the city is the best.
East—west—city's best.

2

Giant buildings made of brick,
elevators go up quick.
Up—down—make it quick!

4

Music, dancing, friends to meet,
spinning feet step to the beat.
Sing—dance—to the beat.

Under streets, down below,
trains with folks go to and fro.
Trains—folks—to and fro.

5

7

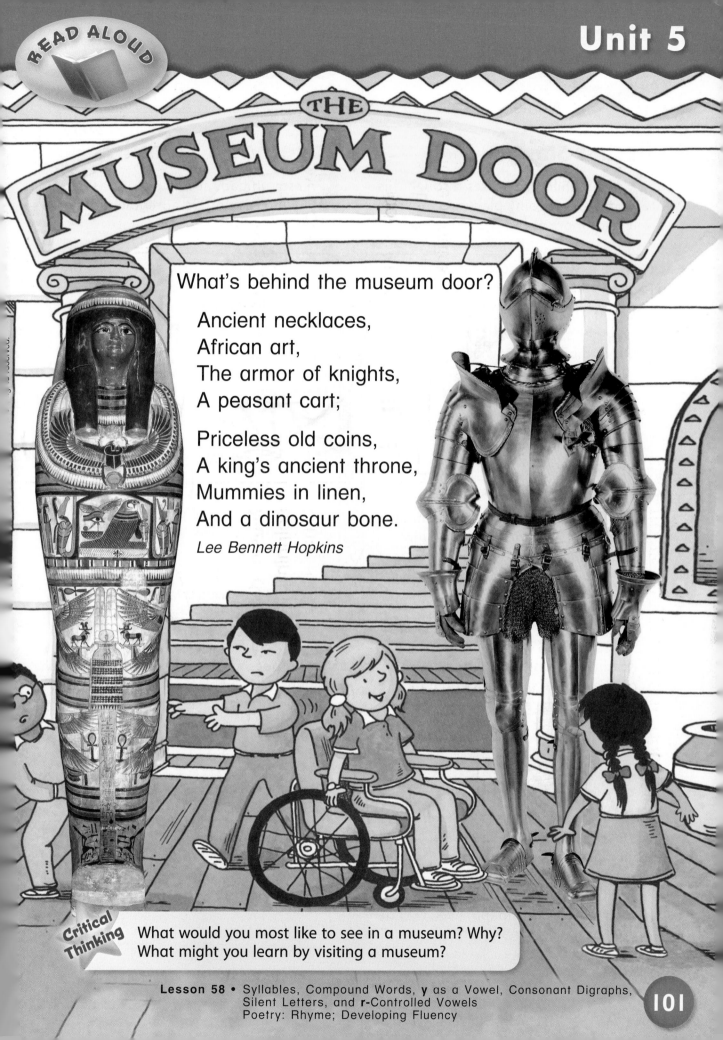

# THE MUSEUM DOOR

What's behind the museum door?

Ancient necklaces,
African art,
The armor of knights,
A peasant cart;

Priceless old coins,
A king's ancient throne,
Mummies in linen,
And a dinosaur bone.

*Lee Bennett Hopkins*

**Critical Thinking** What would you most like to see in a museum? Why?
What might you learn by visiting a museum?

**Lesson 58** • Syllables, Compound Words, **y** as a Vowel, Consonant Digraphs,
Silent Letters, and **r**-Controlled Vowels
Poetry: Rhyme; Developing Fluency

# Dear Family,

**A**s your child progresses through this unit about going places, he or she will learn more about the following:

**syllable:** word or word part with one vowel sound; words can have one or more syllables (**wag, wagon**)

**compound word:** word made up of two or more smaller words (**raincoat**)

**silent letters:** letters whose sounds are not said (**k**now, com**b**)

**words with y as a vowel:** words in which y has the sound of long **i** or long **e** (fl**y**, cit**y**)

**words ending in le:** (app**le**)

**consonant digraph:** two consonants together that stand for one sound (**ch**in, too**th**)

**words with ar, or, er, ir, ur:** words in which **r** gives the vowel a new sound (b**ar**n, c**or**n, f**er**n, b**ir**d, t**ur**n)

• Read the poem "The Museum Door" on the reverse side. Talk about interesting places you and your child have visited.

# Apreciada Familia,

**E**n esta unidad, acerca de los paseos, su niño continuará aprendiendo sobre:

**sílaba:** pálabra o parte de una palabra que tiene un sonido vocal; las palabras pueden tener una o más sílabas (**wagon:** dos sonidos vocales = dos sílabas)

**palabras compuestas:** aquellas formadas por dos o más palabras (**raincoat**)

**letra y con sonido de vocal:** palabras en las que la y tiene el sonido largo de la i o la e (fl**y**, cit**y**)

**palabras que terminan en le:** (app**le**)

**consonantes dígrafas:** dos consonantes juntas que producen un solo sonido (**ch**in, too**th**)

**palabras con ar, or, er, ir, ur:** palabras donde la letra r da a la vocal un nuevo sonido (b**ar**n, c**or**n, f**er**n, b**ir**d, t**ur**n)

• Lea la poesía "The Museum Door" en la página 101. Hablen de los otros lugares interesantes que hayan visitado.

## PROJECT

## PROYECTO

**W**ith your child, make a map of an imaginary town. As your child learns new words in this unit, use them to make up place names for the map. Help your child label the map.

**D**ibujen el mapa de un pueblo imaginario. Con las palabras aprendidas en esta unidad busquen nombres para el mapa. Ayude al niño a rotular el mapa.

**102**

**Lesson 58** • Syllables, Compound Words, **y** as a Vowel, Consonant Digraphs, Silent Letters, and **r**-Controlled Vowels—Phonics Alive at Home

 Visit us at **www.sadlierphonicsonline.co**

Name _____

**Write** the compound word from the box
that fits each clue.

| anthill | beanbag | beehive | rowboat | seaweed | snowflake |

1. This is a boat you row.  _____

2. This is a hive for bees.  _____

3. This is a hill made by ants.  _____

4. This is a weed that grows in the sea.  _____

5. This is a flake of snow.  _____

6. This is a bag filled with beans.  _____

**Write i** next to each word in which **y** has the long **i** sound. **Write e** next to each
word in which **y** has the long **e** sound.

| 7. _____ | 8. _____ | 9. _____ | 10. _____ |
|---|---|---|---|
| fly _____ | city _____ | try _____ | daisy _____ |
| 11. _____ | 12. _____ | 13. _____ | 14. _____ |
| candy _____ | penny _____ | dry _____ | why _____ |

 **Check-Up** Make compound words. **Draw** a line from each word in the first column to a word in the second column. **Write** the new word.

| | |
|---|---|
| ant ● | ● cake |
| tree ● | ● hill |
| pea ● | ● ball |
| base ● | ● top |
| pan ● | ● nut |

| | |
|---|---|
| her ● | ● bow |
| in ● | ● end |
| tea ● | ● self |
| rain ● | ● side |
| week ● | ● cup |

1. _____

2. _____

3. _____

4. _____

5. _____

6. _____

7. _____

8. _____

9. _____

10. _____

**Check-Up** **Circle** the words in which **y** has the same sound as the picture name.

11.

| sky | by |
|---|---|
| bunny | city |
| penny | why |
| **Long i** try | cry |

12.

| dry | twenty |
|---|---|
| forty | ugly |
| pony | my |
| **Long e** fly | candy |

 **PHONICS ALIVE AT HOME** Review this Check-Up with your child.

Spell, Write, and Tell

Say, spell, and talk about each word in the box. Write each word under the digraph or silent letter in its name. Circle the digraph or silent letter.

thorn

truck

chose

wrote

peach

why

knee

show

black

wash

both

what

1. **th**

2. **sh**

3. **wh**

4. **ch**

5. **ck**

6. **kn**

7. **wr**

**Spell, Write, and Tell** Welcome a visitor to your favorite place and tell about it. **Write** what you would say. Use one or more of the words in the box. **Read** your speech aloud.

| thorn | truck | chose | wrote | peach | why |
|-------|-------|-------|-------|-------|-----|
| knee | show | black | wash | both | what |

## Welcome to

Visit **www.sadlierphonicsonline.com** for another activity with consonant digraph

Name _____

★ Look at the picture clues. Write the words in the puzzles.

**DOWN** ⬇

1.

2.

**ACROSS** ➡  3.    4.

**DOWN** ⬇

5.

6.

**ACROSS** ➡  7.    8.

Check-Up

Circle the consonant digraph or silent letters that **begin** the picture name.

| 1. | | 2. | | 3. | |
|---|---|---|---|---|---|
| | th | | wr | | th |
| | sh | | ch | | kn |
| | wh | | wh | | wr |

| 4. | | 5. | | 6. | |
|---|---|---|---|---|---|
| | wr | | sh | | sh |
| | sh | | kn | | th |
| | wh | | ch | | ch |

| 7. | | 8. | | 9. | |
|---|---|---|---|---|---|
| | sh | | th | | wr |
| | wh | | kn | | sh |
| | ch | | wh | | wh |

Check-Up

Circle the consonant digraph that **ends** the picture name.

| 10. | | 11. | | 12. | |
|---|---|---|---|---|---|
| | th | | ck | | th |
| | sh | | th | | sh |
| | ch | | sh | | ch |

| 13. | | 14. | | 15. | |
|---|---|---|---|---|---|
| | ck | | th | | ck |
| | th | | sh | | sh |
| | ch | | ch | | ch |

PHONICS ALIVE AT HOME

Review this Check-U with your child.

Name _____

**Spell, Write, and Tell**

Say, **spell**, and **talk** about each word in the box. **Write** each word under the correct heading.

| before |
|--------|
| clerk |
| far |
| first |
| girl |
| her |
| herd |
| horse |
| purse |
| start |
| store |
| turn |

**1.** **er** words

_____
_____
_____
_____
_____

**2.** **or** words

_____
_____
_____
_____
_____

**3.** **ar** words

_____
_____
_____

**4.** **ir** words

_____
_____
_____
_____

**5.** **ur** words

_____
_____
_____
_____

Visit **www.sadlierphonicsonline.com**
for another activity with **r**-controlled vowels.

Lesson 80 • Connecting Spelling, Writing, and Speaking

**133**

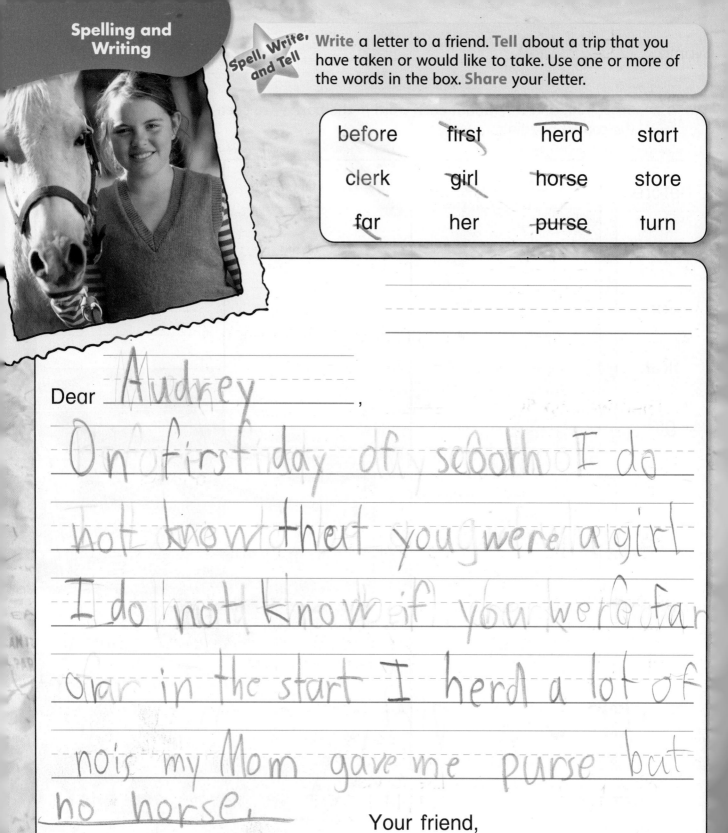

**Spell, Write, and Tell**

**Write** a letter to a friend. **Tell** about a trip that you have taken or would like to take. Use one or more of the words in the box. **Share** your letter.

| | | | |
|---|---|---|---|
| before | first | herd | start |
| clerk | girl | horse | store |
| far | her | purse | turn |

Dear Audrey,

On first day of school I do
not know that you were a girl
I do not know if you were far
orar in the start I herd a lot of
nois my Mom gave me purse but
no horse.

Your friend,

Elena

PHONICS ALIVE AT HOME

Ask your child to read his or her letter to you and to name the **er** words, **ir** words, and **ur** words

Name _____

**READ**  Read the page. Talk about the Statue of Liberty.

## Learn About the Statue of Liberty

Meet Lady Liberty. That's what some people call this statue. Lady Liberty stands on an island in New York Harbor. She greets people who come to the United States. Lady Liberty was a gift to us from the people of France. She's 154 feet high and stands on a base that's 15 feet high. Did you know you can climb almost all the way up? Lady Liberty holds the torch of freedom above her head.

Why do you think Lady Liberty holds the torch of freedom above her head?

Lesson 82 • Syllables, Compound Words, **y** as a Vowel, Consonant Digraphs, Silent Letters, and **r**-Controlled Vowels in Context
Comprehension: Drawing Conclusions
Developing Fluency

137

**Phonics and Writing**

# Going Somewhere?

If you could use a time-travel machine, when and where would you travel to? **Write** about it. Use one or more words from the box.

## Writer's Tips

• Make a list of all the places you'd like to time-travel to. Rank the places in the order you'd like to visit them. Write about the first one.

• Be specific about why you'd like go there.

| travel | local | robot | future | distant |
|--------|-------|-------|--------|---------|
| pilot | ever | custom | planet | dusty |

Place: _____

_____

_____

Time period: _____

_____

_____

Why: _____

_____

_____

**Lesson 83** • Writing VCCV and VCV Words in Context

**PHONICS ALIVE AT HOME** Have your child circle all the VCCV words he or she used and draw a box around the VCV words he or she used.

# Magic Carpet Ride

— Fold —

1

**Reading at Home:** After reading the book together, ask your child to retell the story. Then look for words with the letters **th, sh, wh, ch, ck, wr,** or **kn.** Also look for compound words, such as **inside** or **anywhere.**

---

I will take you anywhere you wish to go

Inside the trunk under some shirts was a purple carpet. The note on the carpet said, "I will take you anywhere you wish to go."

— Fold —

3

---

If you had a magic carpet, where would you go? Draw a picture and write about it.

8

— Fold —

Then the children visited China. They saw a furry panda eating bamboo.

6

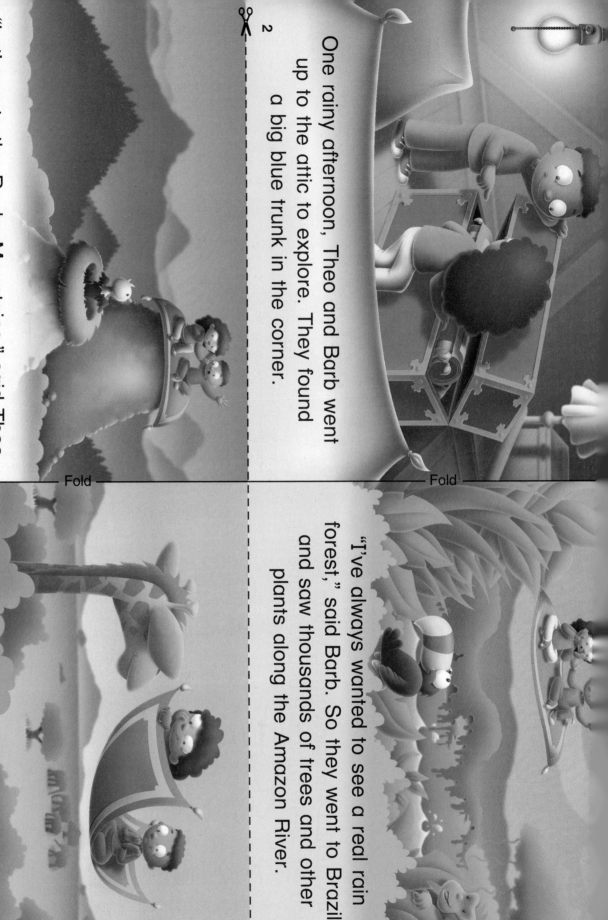

One rainy afternoon, Theo and Barb went up to the attic to explore. They found a big blue trunk in the corner.

— Fold —

"I've always wanted to see a real rain forest," said Barb. So they went to Brazil and saw thousands of trees and other plants along the Amazon River.

"Let's go to the Rocky Mountains," said Theo. With a swish, they began to fly over the treetops. They landed on a beautiful mountaintop.

— Fold —

Next they went to Tanzania. They saw giraffes, elephants, and lions. "I didn't know that giraffes were so tall," said Barb.

# WHAT IS BROWN?

Brown is the color of
  a country road
Back of a turtle
Back of a toad.
Brown is cinnamon
And morning toast
And the good smell of
The Sunday roast.
Brown is the color of work
And the sound of a river,
Brown is bronze and a bow
And a quiver.
Brown is the house
On the edge of town
Where wind is tearing
The shingles down.

*Mary O'Neill*

**Critical Thinking** How would you color the things outside your home?
What does your favorite color make you think of?

Name _____

# Dear Family,

**A**s your child progresses through this unit about colors, she or he will learn about vowel digraphs and diphthongs.

> **vowel digraph:** two letters that come together to make a long sound, a short sound, or a special sound (**br<u>ea</u>d, h<u>oo</u>k, p<u>au</u>se, l<u>aw</u>n**)
>
> **diphthong:** two letters blended together to make one vowel sound (**br<u>ow</u>n, h<u>ou</u>se, c<u>oi</u>n, t<u>oy</u>**)

- Read the poem "What Is Brown?" on the reverse side. Talk about other colors that you see every day.

- With your child, take turns reading words from the poem that rhyme. (**road/toad, toast/roast, river/quiver, town/down**)

- Help your child find words in the poem that have vowel digraphs or diphthongs. (**br<u>ow</u>n, g<u>oo</u>d, s<u>ou</u>nd, h<u>ou</u>se, t<u>ow</u>n, d<u>ow</u>n**)

# Apreciada Familia,

**E**n esta unidad, sobre los colores, su niño aprenderá vocales dígrafas y los diptongos.

> **vocales dígrafas:** dos letras que al unirse producen un sonido largo, corto o especial (**br<u>ea</u>d, h<u>oo</u>k, p<u>au</u>se, l<u>aw</u>n**)
>
> **diptongos:** dos letras que al unirse producen un sonido (**br<u>ow</u>n, h<u>ou</u>se, c<u>oi</u>n, t<u>oy</u>**)

- Lea la poesía "What Is Brown?" en la página 143. Hablen de los colores que ven todos los días.

- Túrnense para leer palabras que rimen en el poema. (**road/toad, toast/roast, river/quiver, town/down**)

- Ayude al niño a encontrar palabras en el poema con vocales dígrafas y diptongos. (**br<u>ow</u>n, g<u>oo</u>d, s<u>ou</u>nd, h<u>ou</u>se, t<u>ow</u>n, d<u>ow</u>n**)

## PROJECT

**T**ogether, draw a rainbow on a large sheet of paper. When your child learns a word that has a vowel digraph or diphthong, suggest that he or she write it under the rainbow. Help your child practice reading the words and using them in sentences.

## PROYECTO

**P**ida al niño que dibuje un arco iris en un papel grande. Cuando el niño aprenda palabras con vocales dígrafas o diptongos puede escribirlas debajo del arco iris. Luego puede practicar leyendo y usando las palabras en oraciones.

Name _____

The vowel digraph **ea** can stand for the short **e** sound, as in **bread**. **Listen** for the sound of short **e** in the rhyme.

My sister Pam made breakfast—
bread with green pea spread,
blue soup with pink potatoes—
I think I'll read instead.

**Here's a Hint!**
A **vowel digraph** is two letters together that stand for one vowel sound. The vowel sound can be long or short, or the vowel digraph can have a sound of its own.

**Say** the name of the picture. **Circle** and **write** its name. **Color** the pictures in which **ea** has the short **e** sound.

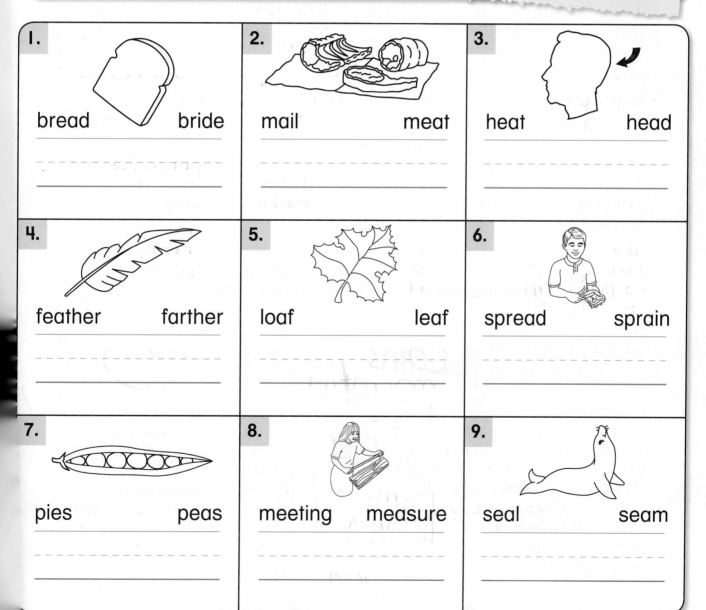

| 1. | 2. | 3. |
|---|---|---|
| bread          bride | mail          meat | heat          head |

| 4. | 5. | 6. |
|---|---|---|
| feather          farther | loaf          leaf | spread          sprain |

| 7. | 8. | 9. |
|---|---|---|
| pies          peas | meeting     measure | seal          seam |

**Read** the story. **Underline** the words in which **ea** has the long **e** sound. **Write** the words in which **ea** has the short **e** sound.

# Welcome to Rainbow Land

Jean grabbed a leather coat. Joan grabbed a sweater. They went out after breakfast. Something was wrong! The sky was pink instead of blue. The leaves on the trees were silver.

"I'm not ready for this," Jean said. "I'm going back to bed."

"Wait," said Joan. "There's a trail of yellow beans. Let's see where they lead."

Jean and Joan followed the trail to a peach meadow. Just ahead they saw a green gingerbread house.

---

**Write on Track**

What happened next? Write about it. Try to use some of these words: **feather, heavy, spread, thread, weather.**

PHONICS ALIVE AT HOME

With your child, look in a newspaper or magazine for words with **ea** that have short **e** sound, such as **head** or **instead**.

Name _____

Say, spell, and talk about each word in the box. Write each word under the vowels in its name.

| | |
|---|---|
| about | |
| because | |
| brown | |
| drew | |
| how | |
| join | |
| look | |
| news | |
| saw | |
| spools | |
| thread | |
| toys | |

1. **ea**

2. **oo**

3. **au**

**aw**

4. **ow**

**ou**

5. **oi**

**oy**

6. **ew**

## Spelling and Writing

**Spell, Write, and Tell** Think of something you can make from spools. **Write** a paragraph to describe it. Use one or more of the words in the box. **Tell** a partner what you chose to describe.

| | | | | | |
|---|---|---|---|---|---|
| about | because | brown | drew | how | join |
| look | news | saw | spools | thread | toys |

**Lesson 95** • Connecting Spelling, Writing, and Speaking

**PHONICS ALIVE AT HOME** Help your child write directions for making the object he or she describe

Name _____

 **Read** Use a word from the box to complete each sentence.
Then practice **reading** the sentences aloud.

| Before | both | fast | off | sleep | wish |
|--------|------|------|-----|-------|------|

1. _____ bedtime, I drew a yellow sun in a blue sky.

2. But I cannot _____ with a bright sun in my room.

3. How _____ can I draw a night sky instead?

4. I will draw _____ a moon and a star.

5. I will make a _____ on the star.

6. Then I will turn _____ my light and sleep!

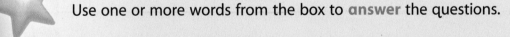 Use one or more words from the box to **answer** the questions.

7. What do you do before you go to sleep at night?

_____

_____

8. What do you wish you had in your room?

_____

_____

**Review**

Circle the word in the box that completes
each sentence. **Write** the word on the line.
**Read** the sentences.

| | |
|---|---|
| **1.** Do you _____ you could draw this bug? | would wish work |
| **2.** Draw an outline of the bug _____ . | both use first |
| **3.** Then _____ a red crayon to color it in. | before use its |
| **4.** You can draw its towel on or keep it _____ . | sleep very off |
| **5.** See how _____ your bug takes shape? | fast wish first |
| **6.** You will be an artist _____ you know it! | both before sleep |

PHONICS
ALIVE AT HOME

Ask your child to draw a picture of a favorite
toy. Then ask him or her to describe it to you
using some of the words in the word box.

# COLORS ALL AROUND

1

3

White is snow that covers the street.

Fold

Fold

Blue is the sea where fish swim around, moving so smoothly without a sound.

8

Brown is a deer with her spotted fawn.

6

**DIRECTIONS:** Cut and fold the book.

Green is a leaf in a meadow moist with dew.

Red is a strawberry, both juicy and sweet.

— Fold —

Fold

Orange is the pumpkin whose face I drew.

Yellow is the sun that we see at dawn.

Lesson 100 • Unit 6 Take-Home Book
Comprehension: Recalling Details

# Numbers, Numbers

Numbers in the grocery store
   About the things we eat,
Numbers on the doorways,
   And in the city street.

Numbers on the calendar,
   On signs that flash or glow,
Numbers on the telephone,
   Or tickets for the show.

Numbers on the buses,
   On money that I spend,
Numbers on the stamps I put
   On letters that I send.

Numbers on the highways, yes
   And numbers in a book!
It seems I'm seeing numbers
   Almost everywhere I look!

*Lee Blair*

**Critical Thinking**
Why are numbers important in your life?
What problems would people have
if there were no numbers?

**Lesson 101** • Contractions, Abbreviations, Plurals, and Inflectional Endings
Poetry: Rhyme
Developing Fluency

Name _____

# Dear Family,

**A**s your child progresses through this unit about numbers, he or she will learn about contractions, abbreviations, plurals, and word endings **s, ed,** and **ing.**

> **contraction:** two words written as one with one or more letters left out **(isn't = is not; I'll = I will)**
>
> **abbreviation:** a shortened form of a word **(Mrs., Blvd.)**
>
> **plural:** word that means more than one **(book<u>s</u>, peach<u>es</u>)**
>
> **word endings s, ed, ing:** endings that can be added to a word to make new words **(need<u>s</u>, help<u>ed</u>, skipp<u>ed</u>, jump<u>ing</u>, bak<u>ing</u>)**

- Read the poem "Numbers, Numbers" on the reverse side. Talk about places where you see numbers.

- Together, look for words in the poem that are plurals, such as **numbers** and **buses.** Also find the contraction **I'm** and the word that ends in **ing, seeing.**

# Apreciada Familia,

**E**n esta unidad, sobre los números, su niño aprenderá sobre contracciones, abreviaturas, el plural y palabras que terminan en **s, ed,** y **ing.**

> **contracción:** una palabra formada por la abreviación de dos palabras **(isn't = is not; I'll = I will)**
>
> **abreviatura:** la forma corta de una palabra **(Mrs., Blvd.)**
>
> **plural:** palabras que indican más de uno **(book<u>s</u>, peach<u>es</u>)**
>
> **palabras que terminan en s, ed, ing:** terminaciones que se añaden al final de una palabra **(need<u>s</u>, help<u>ed</u>, skipp<u>ed</u>, jump<u>ing</u>, bak<u>ing</u>)**

- Lea la poesía "Numbers, Numbers" en la página 169. Hablen de los lugares donde ven números.

- Juntos busquen en el poema palabras en plural, como por ejemplo: **numbers** y **buses.** También busquen la contracción **I'm** y la palabra que termina en **ing, seeing.**

## PROJECT

**H**elp your child make a word bank by putting a slit in the top of a shoebox. When your child learns a new contraction, abbreviation, plural word, or word that ends in **s, ed,** or **ing,** have him or her write the word on a card and "deposit" it in the bank.

## PROYECTO

**H**agan un banco de palabras con una caja de zapatos. Cada vez que el niño aprenda una contracción, una abreviatura, un plural, o una palabra que termine en **s, ed,** o **ing,** pídale que la escriba en una tarjeta y la "deposite" en el banco. El niño puede "retirar" palabras para escribir oraciones.

 Visit us at **www.sadlierphonicsonline.com**

Name _____

**Work Together**

With a partner, **write** the contraction for each pair of words. Take turns **reading** the pair of words and then the contraction.

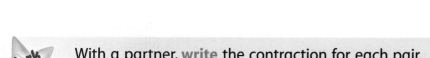

**Here's a Hint!**
Some **contractions** are formed with **am, is,** and **are.**
**I'm** = I + **am**
**he's** = he + **is**
**we're** = we + **are**

| he's | I'm | it's | she's | that's |
| they're | we're | what's | you're |

| 1. | I am | 2. | he is | 3. | we are |
|---|---|---|---|---|---|
| | | | | | |
| 4. | that is | 5. | she is | 6. | they are |
| | | | | | |
| 7. | it is | 8. | what is | 9. | you are |
| | | | | | |

**Write** the words for the underlined contraction in each sentence.

10. <u>I'm</u> going to run in a race. _____

11. <u>It's</u> a two-mile run. _____

# Contractions

Here's a Hint!
Some **contractions** are formed with **have, has,** and **us**.
**she's** = she + **is** or she + **has**
**you've** = you + **have**
**let's** = let + **us**

Write the contraction for each pair of words.

| he's | it's | I've | let's |
|------|------|------|-------|
| she's | they've | we've | you've |

**1.** she has
_____

**2.** you have
_____

**3.** let us
_____

**4.** we have
_____

**5.** he has
_____

**6.** I have
_____

**7.** they have
_____

**8.** it has
_____

Write the words for the underlined contraction in each sentence.

**9.** <u>I've</u> a new game we can play.
_____

**10.** <u>You've</u> scored thirty points.
_____

**11.** <u>It's</u> been fun playing with you.
_____

PHONICS ALIVE AT HOME
Make up a sentence with **I have, you have,** or **they have.** Ask your child to replace the two words with a contraction.

Name _____

**Spell, Write, and Tell** Say, spell, and talk about each word in the box. Write each word under the correct heading.

can't

didn't

I'll

it's

I've

let's

shouldn't

that's

they've

we've

what's

you'll

**1.** Contractions with **not**

**2.** Contractions with **is**

**3.** Contractions with **have**

**4.** Contractions with **will**

**5.** Contractions with **us**

7:30 A.M.

Visit www.sadlierphonicsonline.com for another activity with contractions.

**Spell, Write, and Tell**

Imagine that your classroom clock could talk. **Write** what it would say. Use one or more of the words in the box. **Give** your speech.

| can't | didn't | I'll | it's | I've | let's |
|---|---|---|---|---|---|
| shouldn't | that's | they've | we've | what's | you'll |

PHONICS ALIVE AT HOME

Ask your child questions as if he or she were the classroom clock. Tell your child to answer using words from the box.

Name _____

Use the number code to **write** contractions. **Write** the letter for each number.
**Write** an apostrophe in the blank space. **Write** the words for each contraction.

| | | | | |
|---|---|---|---|---|
| 1 = **a** | 2 = **d** | 3 = **e** | 4 = **h** | 5 = **i** |
| 6 = **l** | 7 = **n** | 8 = **o** | 9 = **r** | 10 = **s** |
| 11 = **t** | 12 = **u** | 13 = **v** | 14 = **w** | 15 = **y** |

**1.** i s n ' t
5  10  7   11

is   not

**2.** ___ ___  ___ ___
14   3    13   3

**3.** ___ ___ ___  ___ ___
15   8   12   9   3

**4.** ___ ___ ___  ___ ___
10   4   3    6   6

**5.** ___ ___ ___ ___  ___
2   5   2   7    11

**6.** ___ ___ ___ ___  ___ ___
11   4   3   15    9   3

**7.** ___ ___ ___ ___  ___
1   9   3   7    11

**8.** ___ ___ ___  ___
6   3   11    10

**Check-Up** **Draw** a line from each contraction to the pair of words it means.

| | | | |
|---|---|---|---|
| 1. he'll ● | ● she will | 9. wasn't ● | ● will not |
| 2. she'll ● | ● he has | 10. you're ● | ● was not |
| 3. he's ● | ● she has | 11. won't ● | ● you have |
| 4. she's ● | ● he will | 12. you've ● | ● you are |
| 5. can't ● | ● we are | 13. I'm ● | ● it has |
| 6. couldn't ● | ● can not | 14. I've ● | ● I will |
| 7. we've ● | ● could not | 15. it's ● | ● I am |
| 8. we're ● | ● we have | 16. I'll ● | ● I have |

**Check-Up** **Underline** the contraction in each sentence. **Write** the words for the contraction.

17. What's your new room number? _____

18. I don't know mine yet. _____

19. Tony can't find his room. _____

20. I'll help him look for it. _____

21. I think it's down the hall. _____

**PHONICS ALIVE AT HOME** Review this Check-U with your child.

Name _____

Jay St. Bus

Jay St.

Jay Street Bus

The abbreviation for **Street** is **St.** The abbreviation for **Mister** is **Mr.** Draw a line from each abbreviation to the word that was shortened.

**Here's a Hint!**

An abbreviation is a shortened form of a word. It uses just a few letters of the word and always ends with a period.

**Road = Rd.**     **December = Dec.**
**Doctor = Dr.**    **Wednesday = Wed.**

| | | |
|---|---|---|
| 1. Rd. ● | ● Friday | 5. Mrs. ●    ● Mister |
| 2. Mar. ● | ● feet | 6. Dr. ●    ● tablespoon |
| 3. Fri. ● | ● Road | 7. Mr. ●    ● Missus |
| 4. ft. ● | ● March | 8. Tbsp. ●    ● Doctor |

Use an abbreviation from the box to complete each sentence.

| Mrs. | Oct. | Mr. | Tues. |
|---|---|---|---|

9. _____ White washed his car.

10. I asked _____ Berg where she got her dress.

11. My brother was born on _____ 27, 2007.

12. Today's date is _____ , May 3.

## Abbreviations

**Write** the word for the underlined abbreviation.

1. The school I go to is on West Park <u>Rd.</u>

_____

2. My math teacher is <u>Mrs.</u> Hiles.

_____

3. The bus stop is 150 <u>ft.</u> from my house.

_____

4. Today is the first <u>Wed.</u> of the month.

_____

**Write** the abbreviation for each word.

| Feb. | Mon. | yd. | ft. | lb. | tsp. | U.S. | Sat. | Apr. |
| --- | --- | --- | --- | --- | --- | --- | --- | --- |

| 5. yard | 6. United States | 7. February |
| --- | --- | --- |
| _____ | _____ | _____ |
| 8. pound | 9. Saturday | 10. feet |
| _____ | _____ | _____ |
| 11. teaspoon | 12. April | 13. Monday |
| _____ | _____ | _____ |

Take a walk with your child and point out abbreviations you see. Ask your child to tell you what the abbreviations stand for.

**180** Lesson 106 • Recognizing and Writing Common Abbreviations

Name _Elena_

Say the name of the picture. Write the plural name. Read the shaded letters down to find the answer to the question.

1.  b e n c h e s

2.  k n i f e s

3.  p e n n y e s

4.  d r e s s e s

5.  f o x e s

6.  w r e n c h e s

7. 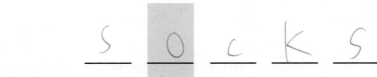 g o s e s

8.  s o c k s

9.  r a b i t e s

10.  m a n

## What number should you call in an emergency?

_____ _____ _____

_____ _____ _____

**Check-Up** **Write** the plural of each word. Remember to make spelling changes if you need to.

| | | |
|---|---|---|
| **1.** pony<br>_ponies_ | **2.** trunk<br>_trunks_ | **3.** shelf<br>_shelfs_ |
| **4.** box<br>_boxes_ | **5.** child<br>_childs_ | **6.** fly<br>_flies_ |
| **7.** foot<br>_foots_ | **8.** peach<br>_peaches_ | **9.** straw<br>_straw_ |

**Check-Up** **Change** the word in **bold** print so that it makes sense in each sentence.

10. There are 10 **penny** in a dime.  _Pennies_

11. Some **fly** only live about 2 hours.  _flies_

12. **Fox** live about 7 years.  _Foxes_

13. Newborn **baby** have 300 bones.  _babies_

14. There are more than 700 kinds of **mouse.**  _mouses_

PHONICS ALIVE AT HOME   Review this Check-U with your child.

Name _____

**Say** each word. **Write** the number of syllables you hear. **Answer** the question below.

| s or es | | ing | | ed | |
|---|---|---|---|---|---|
| **1.** walks | 1 | walking | 2 | walked | 1 |
| **2.** tries | 1 | trying | 2 | tried | 1 |
| **3.** races | 1 | racing | 2 | raced | 1 |
| **4.** votes | 1 | voting | 2 | voted | 1 |
| **5.** shops | 1 | shopping | 2 | shopped | 1 |

**6.** How many syllables are in words with endings?
**Circle** the best answer.

always one          always two          one or more

**Add ed** or **ing** to each root word and **write** the new word.
Make spelling changes as necessary.

bake    **7.** We are ___baking___ muffins today.

mix    **8.** I ___mixing___ two cups of flour and water.

place    **9.** Dad just ___place___ the pan in the oven.

**Read and Write**

Read the number log that Jamal kept for math class. Answer the questions.

## Numbers All Around

### At Home

- I used the numbers on my watch to get to school on time. I started walking at 7:15.

- I invited Grandma for dinner by calling her phone number. She'll be coming at 7:00 tonight.

- I didn't forget Gary's birthday. I looked at the calendar. It's tomorrow—March 29th! He'll be nine.

### At School

- I got to my classroom by finding a 4 on the door.

- I found my math lesson by turning to page 133.

- I kept score during soccer by counting the goals.

**Foxes: 3  Ponies: 6**

**1.** Name one way Jamal used numbers at home.

_____

_____

**2.** How do numbers help you at home?

_____

_____

**PHONICS ALIVE AT HOME**  With your child, keep a number log. Think of ways to group your finding

Name _Elena_

**Spell, Write, and Tell** Say, spell, and talk about each word in the box. Write each word under the correct heading.

| | |
|---|---|
| brushes | |
| carried | |
| hurried | |
| jogging | |
| jumping | |
| raked | |
| running | |
| smiling | |
| stopped | |
| tries | |
| washed | |
| wiped | |

**1. No Root Changes**

jumping

brushes

washed

**2. Change y to i**

carried

tries

hurried

**3. Drop Final e**

smiling

raked

wiped

**4. Double Final Consonant**

jogging

stopped

running

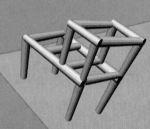

Spelling and Writing

**Spell, Write, and Tell** Read the playground rhyme. Add one or two verses. Use one or more of the words in the box. Share your rhyme with the class.

| brushes | carried | hurried | jogging | jumping | raked |
| running | smiling | stopped | tries | washed | wiped |

I went outside to count the stars.

I made a mistake and counted cars.

I went inside to bake a pie.

I made a mistake and baked a fly.

They carried a shovel and

PHONICS ALIVE AT HOME Ask your child to read the rhyme he or she wrote. Together, make up a new verse using some of the words in the box.

Name _____

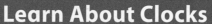

**Read** the page. **Talk** about clocks.

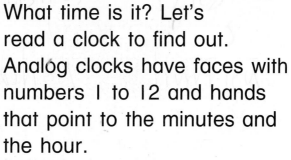
## Learn About Clocks

What time is it? Let's read a clock to find out. Analog clocks have faces with numbers 1 to 12 and hands that point to the minutes and the hour.

Digital clocks don't have hands. A symbol (:) separates the hour and minutes. The number before the symbol tells the hour. The number after the symbol tells the minutes past the hour.

What would happen if people didn't have clocks or watches?

**Lesson 120** • Contractions, Abbreviations, Plurals, and Inflectional Endings in Context
Comprehension: Understanding Cause and Effect
Developing Fluency

199

# Numbers Everywhere

### Writer's Tips

- Start by telling what you'd like to be.
- Give at least two examples of how you will use numbers in your job.

How might numbers be a part of what you want to do when you grow up? **Write** about it. Use one or more words from the box.

| | | | | |
|---|---|---|---|---|
| halves | adding | ft. | yds. | lbs. |
| subtracted | billing | makes | building | tried |

Lesson 121 • Writing Abbreviations, Irregular Plurals, and Inflectional Endings in Context

Have your child underline all the words that have endings. Then ask your child to circle the root words.

Name _____

Check-Up

**Add** the ending at the top to each root word in the column. **Write** the new word.

| s or es | ing | ed |
|---|---|---|
| 1. clean | 4. bake | 7. stop |
| 2. mix | 5. know | 8. jump |
| 3. cry | 6. drip | 9. wipe |

Check-Up

**Underline** the word that ends in **ing** or **ed** in each sentence.
**Write** the root word.

10. At 4:30 A.M., Tina's alarm clock buzzed. _____

11. She tried to make it stop. _____

12. It was too early to be waking up! _____

# Assessment

 **Check-Up** Add the ending at the top to each root word and **write** the word.

| | s or es | ed | ing |
|---|---|---|---|
| **1.** rain | | | |
| **2.** fix | | | |
| **3.** slip | | | |
| **4.** pile | | | |
| **5.** dry | | | |
| **6.** carry | | | |
| **7.** help | | | |
| **8.** vote | | | |
| **9.** pass | | | |
| **10.** marry | | | |

PHONICS ALIVE AT HOME Review this Check-U with your child.

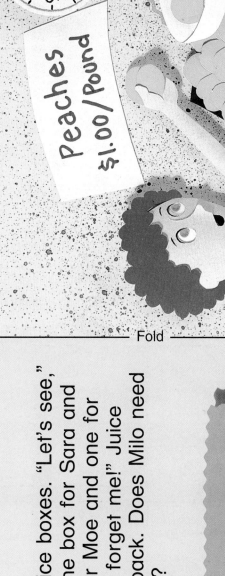

GROCERY STORE

FRUIT

PEARS 99¢

---

— 1

Reading at Home: Read the book with your child and answer the questions. Have your child find the plural for **peach (peaches)** and **apple (apples)**. Then look for contractions, such as **let's**, and a word that ends with **ing (shopping)**.

---

Peaches
$1.00/Pound

3

---

**Fold**

---

Milo pays for his groceries. The cashier says, "Here's 29 cents change." Which coins should Milo get?

8

---

2 dimes, 1 nickel, 4 pennies

Thanks for helping Milo!

---

**Fold**

---

no

There's a sale on juice boxes. "Let's see," Milo says. "I'll get one box for Sara and one for Tara, one for Moe and one for Joe. Oh, and I can't forget me!" Juice boxes come 6 to a pack. Does Milo need more than one pack?

yes    no

9

---

**DIRECTIONS:** Cut and fold the book.

Lesson 123 • Unit 7 Take-Home Book
Comprehension: Drawing Conclusions

203

Let's help Milo with his shopping.
Circle the best answer to each question.

Milo says, "I'll start with fruit." One pound of peaches costs $1.00. Milo gets 3 pounds. How much will he spend on peaches?

$1.00   $3.00   $8.00

$3.00

Milo thinks, "An apple a day keeps the doctor away. Maybe I'll eat an apple every day next week." How many apples should Milo buy for next week?

1 apple   7 apples   12 apples

2 apples

4

Fold

Fold

from
# Swinging

Slowly, slowly, swinging low,
Let me see how far I go!
Slowly, slowly, keeping low,
I see where the wild flowers grow!

(Getting quicker):

Quicker, quicker,
Swinging higher,
I can see
The sunset's fire!

Faster, faster,
Through the air,
I see almost
Everywhere.

(Getting slower):

Slower, slower, now I go,
Swinging, dreaming, getting low;
Slowly, slowly, down I go—
Till I touch the grass below.

*Irene Thompson*

**Critical Thinking** What do you think is the best part about going high on a swing? If you could put a swing anywhere, where would you put it? Why?

Name _____

# Dear Family,

**A**s your child progresses through this unit about outdoor fun, she or he will learn about the following:

**suffix:** word part added to the end of a word to change its meaning or make a new word (care**ful**)

**prefix:** word part added to the beginning of a word to change its meaning or make a new word (**re**load)

**synonyms:** words that have the same meaning (**fast/quick**)

**antonyms:** words that have the opposite meaning (**up/down**)

**homonyms:** words that sound the same, but have different spellings and meanings (**blue/blew**)

- Read the poem "Swinging" on the reverse side. Talk about how your family has outdoor fun.

- Read the poem again, going faster and faster until you reach the last stanza.

- Together, look for words in the poem with the suffixes **ly** and **er**, such as **slowly** and **quicker**.

# Apreciada Familia,

**E**n esta unidad, sobre el recreo, su niño aprenderá los siguientes tipos de palabras y partes de palabras.

**sufijos:** letras que se añaden al final de una palabra y que cambian su significado o hacen una nueva (care**ful**)

**prefijos:** letras que se añaden al principio de una palabra y que cambian su significado o hacen una nueva (**re**load)

**sinónimos:** palabras que tienen el mismo significado (**fast/quick**)

**antónimos:** palabras que significan lo opuesto (**up/down**)

**homónimos:** palabras que tienen el mismo sonido pero diferente significado y se escriben diferente (**blue/blew**)

- Lea "Swinging" en la página 205. Hablen de lo que hace su familia para divertirse fuera de la casa.

- Lea de nuevo el poema, cada vez más rápido, hasta llegar a la última estrofa.

- Busquen palabras en el poema que tengan los sufijos **ly, er,** por ejemplo: **slowly, quicker.**

*up*

*down*

*untie*

*useful*

## PROJECT

**H**elp your child draw a kite and cut it out. Attach a tail. As your child learns new words from this unit, have him or her write the words on small pieces of paper and tape them to the tail.

## PROYECTO

**A**yude a su niño a dibujar y recortar una cometa. Átele una cola. Anime al niño a escribir palabras aprendidas en esta unidad en pedacitos de papel y pegarlas en la cola de la cometa.

Visit us at **www.sadlierphonicsonline.com**

Name _____

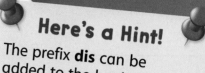

The prefix **dis** means "not" or "opposite of." Use the prefix **dis** to **write** a word for each definition.

| | | |
|---|---|---|
| **1.** not honest | **2.** the opposite of **agree** | **3.** the opposite of **obey** |
| **4.** the opposite of **like** | **5.** not pleased | **6.** the opposite of **appear** |

**Add** the prefix **dis** so that the word in **bold** print makes sense in each sentence. **Write** the new word.

**7.** Ed and I are friends even when we **agree.** _____

**8.** It is **honest** to tell a lie. _____

**9.** Snow **appears** when it gets warm. _____

**Write on Track**

Write one thing you **like** and one thing you **dislike** about the outdoors.

Add the prefix to the root word to **write** a new word. **Say** the word. **Write** the number of syllables you hear.

**1.**
re + read
_____

**2.**
dis + trust
_____

**3.**
dis + like
_____

**4.**
un + lucky
_____

**5.**
un + fair
_____

**6.**
re + open
_____

Circle the prefix in each word. **Answer** the question below.

| | | |
|---|---|---|
| **7.** unchain | **11.** rebuild | **15.** retell |
| **8.** reheat | **12.** dishonest | **16.** uncover |
| **9.** displeased | **13.** unfold | **17.** disapprove |
| **10.** rewrite | **14.** disagree | **18.** unclear |

**19.** How many syllables does each prefix that you circled add to the root word? Circle the best answer.

none                    one                    two

**PHONICS ALIVE AT HOME** Say the words in items 7–18 and ask your child to tell how many syllables he or she hears in each word.

Name _____

 **Write** a word with the prefix **re, un,** or **dis** for each clue.
**Read** down to find the answer to the question.

1. **join** again ___ ___ ___ ___ ___ ___

2. opposite of **tie** ___ ___ ___ ___ ___

3. opposite of **trust** ___ ___ ___ ___ ___ ___ ___

4. **draw** again ___ ___ ___

5. opposite of **load** ___ ___ ___ ___ ___ ___ ___

6. opposite of **obey** ___ ___ ___ ___ ___ ___

7. not **true** ___ ___ ___ ___ ___

8. **fill** again ___ ___ ___ ___ ___ ___

9. **use** again ___ ___ ___ ___

10. not **able** ___ ___ ___ ___ ___ ___

What can you do in the summer sun?

 Have a lot of _____ _____ !

**Check-Up** — Write the root word for each word.

| | | |
|---|---|---|
| **1.** retell <br> tell | **2.** unpack <br> pack | **3.** disobey <br> obey |
| **4.** untie <br> tie | **5.** disagree <br> agree | **6.** recheck <br> check |
| **7.** dishonest <br> honest | **8.** refill <br> fill | **9.** unbutton <br> button |

**Check-Up** — Underline the word in parentheses ( ) that makes sense in each sentence.

10. Mom says that my treehouse is (**unable, unsafe**).

11. That (**disagrees, displeases**) Mom.

12. It makes me (**unhappy, unroll**), too.

13. We have to (**reuse, replace**) wood that has rotted.

14. We have to (**repaint, replay**) the whole thing.

15. I (**dislike, disappear**) this sandpaper.

16. I'm (**untied, unable**) to reach the roof.

17. It's (**unclear, unafraid**) how we'll ever finish.

18. I'd better stop complaining and (**refill, rejoin**) Mom at work.

*PHONICS ALIVE AT HOME*   Review this Check-Up with your child.

Name _____

**Bag** and **sack** are synonyms. **Listen** and **look** for synonyms in the rhyme.

Let's run quickly,
in a bag or a sack.
We'll go very fast,
on a path or a track.

**Fast** and **quick** are synonyms. **Find** and **write** a synonym for each word.

**Here's a Hint!**
**Synonyms** are words that have the same or nearly the same meaning.

| bag | begin | fast | home | jog | large |
|-----|-------|------|------|-----|-------|

| | | |
|---|---|---|
| **1.** quick | **2.** run | **3.** start |
| **4.** big | **5.** sack | **6.** house |

**Draw** a line from each word in the first column to its synonym in the second column.

| | | | |
|---|---|---|---|
| **7.** jump ● | ● happy | **13.** cry ● | ● weep |
| **8.** rush ● | ● leap | **14.** sound ● | ● high |
| **9.** glad ● | ● hurry | **15.** tall ● | ● noise |
| **10.** boat ● | ● kind | **16.** wet ● | ● yell |
| **11.** nice ● | ● close | **17.** sick ● | ● ill |
| **12.** near ● | ● ship | **18.** shout ● | ● damp |

# Synonyms

Circle the word in each list that means the same or nearly the same as the word in **bold** print.

| 1. **home** | 2. **below** | 3. **leave** | 4. **pail** |
|---|---|---|---|
| door | over | stay | bucket |
| house | in | here | spoon |
| car | under | go | water |
| work | out | slow | sink |

Write the word from the box that is a synonym for the word in **bold** print.

| hike | little | pal | tapped | trail |
|---|---|---|---|---|

5. My **friend** Goldie likes to be outdoors.

6. One day Goldie went for a **walk.**

7. She decided to explore a new **path.**

8. She followed the path to a **small** house.

9. Goldie **knocked** on the door.

**Write on Track**

Was anyone home? Finish the story. In your sentences, you might use synonyms for the words **big** and **small.**

Ask your child to read sentences 5– using the synonyms he or she wrote in place of the words in bold print.

Name _____

**High** and **low** are antonyms. **Listen** and **look** for antonyms in the rhyme.

High, low, fast, slow,
over the ocean,
under the sea, hurry up.
Come jump with me.

**Here's a Hint!**
**Antonyms** are words that have the opposite or nearly the opposite meaning.

 **Hot** and **cold** are antonyms. **Find** and **write** an antonym for each word.

| asleep | big | float | hot | left |
|--------|-----|-------|-----|------|
| open | smile | stop | under | |

| | | |
|---|---|---|
| 1. cold | 2. awake | 3. right |
| 4. go | 5. little | 6. over |
| 7. frown | 8. sink | 9. close |

 **Circle** the word in each list that means the opposite of the word in **bold** print.

| 10. **happy** | 11. **clean** | 12. **lost** | 13. **front** |
|---------------|---------------|--------------|---------------|
| good | water | gone | back |
| glad | wash | found | door |
| sad | dirty | under | top |

**Work Together**

**Read** about Cam. Work with a partner to **write** a story about her friend Mac. **Tell** how he is the opposite of Cam. **Replace** each word in **bold** print with an antonym.

Cam is a **tall girl. She** sits in the **last** row of **her** class. **She** has **long** hair and freckles. **She always** wears glasses. When **she** writes, **she** uses **her right** hand.

Cam likes **winter** sports. **She** enjoys skating. Even on the **coldest** days, you'll find Cam outdoors.

PHONICS ALIVE AT HOME

Ask your child to read each word in bold print and then the antonym he or she wrote. For example: **tall/short, girl/boy**.

Name_____

**Heard** and **herd** are homonyms. **Listen** and **look** for homonyms in the rhyme.

I heard a herd of skunks.
I heard them, I insist!
Though mist hid them from view,
my nose knows what I missed.

**Sail** and **sale** are homonyms. **Find** and **write** a homonym for each word.

| ate | for | not | sail | sun | to |
|-----|-----|-----|------|-----|-----|

| 1. sale | 2. eight | 3. knot |
|---------|----------|---------|
| sail ✓ | ate ✓ | hot ✗ |
| **4.** four | **5.** son | **6.** two |
| for ✓ | sun ✓ | to ✓ |

**Cross out** the word that does not make sense in each sentence.
**Find** and **write** a homonym from above.

**7.** I eight breakfast early in the morning. _____ate_____

**8.** Then I decided to go four a walk. _____for_____

**9.** The son was shining brightly. _____sun_____

**10.** It was a great day two be outdoors. _____to_____

Lesson 136 • Recognizing and Writing Homonyms  **225**

# Homonyms

**Circle** two words in each box that sound the same, but have different spellings and meanings.

| | | | | | |
|---|---|---|---|---|---|
| **1.** | (tale) tall / (tail) tell | **2.** | ride (right) / (write) white | **3.** | reed (road) / ride (rode) |
| **4.** | knot note / (night) (knight) | **5.** | (dear) deep / (deer) deal | **6.** | weed (weak) / (week) wood |

**Work Together**

**Circle** and **write** the word that completes each sentence.
**Compare** answers with a partner.

**7.** Lashanda and I ___made___ little toy boats.     (made)  maid

**8.** Mine was red and hers was ___blue___.     blew  (blue)

**9.** We put paper ___sails___ on the top.     sales  (sails)

**10.** We put our boats in the ___creek___.     creek  creak

**11.** We decided to race ___our___ boats.     hour  (our)

**12.** The wind ___blew___ the sails.     blew  blue

**13.** Lashanda and ___I___ clapped.     eye  I

**14.** Lashanda ___won___ the race.     one  won

**PHONICS ALIVE AT HOME** With your child, make up sentenc using the words he or she did not circle in items 7–14.

Name _____

 Draw a line from a word in the first column to its **synonym** in the second column.

| 1. | home ● | ● nap | 4. | bag ● | ● begin |
| 2. | sleep ● | ● ill | 5. | friend ● | ● pal |
| 3. | sick ● | ● house | 6. | start ● | ● sack |

Draw a line from a word in the first column to its **antonym** in the second column.

| 7. | little ● | ● front | 10. | out ● | ● open |
| 8. | long ● | ● big | 11. | close ● | ● in |
| 9. | back ● | ● short | 12. | awake ● | ● asleep |

**Cross out** the word that does not make sense in each sentence. **Find** and **write** the correct word.

| I | made | new | to | wood |

13. Dad maid a swing for me. _____

14. He used a piece of would for the seat. _____

15. Dad and eye hung the swing in a tree. _____

16. I like my knew swing. _____

17. Watch me swing two and fro. _____

**Read and Write**    **Read** the book report. **Answer** the questions.

Book Report by Leah Siegel

<u>Owl Moon</u> by Jane Yolen

    Whoo! Whoo! Did you ever hear the sound of an owl? In <u>Owl Moon</u> by Jane Yolen, a girl and her father go owling. That means they go looking for owls. It is a snowy night and the woods look scary. But the girl is not afraid. She and her father keep walking and looking.

    You will like this book if you like to read about animals or about doing things outdoors. Read <u>Owl Moon</u> to find out if the girl ever sees an owl. Whoo! Whoo!

**1.** How do you think the girl in *Owl Moon* feels about owling with her father?

_____

- - - - - - - - - - - - - - - - - - - - - - -

_____

**2.** Do you think the person who wrote this book report would read another book by Jane Yolen? Why or why not?

_____

- - - - - - - - - - - - - - - - - - - - - - -

_____

**PHONICS ALIVE AT HOME**   Discuss whether Jane Yolen had know facts about owls to write *Owl Moon*. Why do you think so

Name _____

**Say**, **spell**, and **talk** about each word in the box.
**Write** six pairs of homonyms.

new

blew

sale

too

for

to

sail

night

knew

knight

blue

four

1.

2.

3.

4.

5.

6.

*Spell, Write, and Tell*

**Write** a poem about summer. Use one or more of the words in the box. **Share** your poem with the class.

| new | blew | sale | too | for | to |
|-----|------|------|-----|-----|-----|
| sail | night | knew | knight | blue | four |

**PHONICS ALIVE AT HOME**

With your child, use the words in the bo to write a poem about something you together outside.

Name _____

READ

**Read** the page. **Talk** about Grand Canyon National Park.

20¢

## Learn About the Grand Canyon

It's the biggest. It's the oldest. It's the most unusual. It's Grand Canyon National Park, and it's filled with things to do. You can take a tour bus. You can take a boat. If you're tall enough, you can ride a mule. You can choose a trail and go for a hike. But don't go too far. Remember that anyone who goes down has to climb back up!

Think about hiking down into the Grand Canyon. What would you like most? What would you like least?

Lesson 141 • Suffixes, Prefixes, Synonyms, Antonyms, and Homonyms in Context
Comprehension: Comparing and Contrasting
Developing Fluency

233

## Phonics and Writing

# Come Out and Play

What is your favorite thing to do outside?
Why is it your favorite? **Write** about it.
Use one or more words from the box.

### Writer's Tips

• Clearly state what your favorite thing to play outside is.

• Give several reasons to explain your choice to readers.

| friends | jump | coast | throw | fast |
|---------|------|-------|-------|------|
| buddies | leap | sail | toss | quick |

Name _____

**Check-Up** Circle the word in each list that means the **same** or **nearly the same** as the word in **bold** print.

| 1. **run** | 2. **big** | 3. **glad** | 4. **shout** |
|---|---|---|---|
| walk | small | sleepy | yell |
| legs | large | happy | whisper |
| jog | thin | sad | talk |
| 5. **begin** | 6. **rush** | 7. **noise** | 8. **quick** |
| write | soon | hear | slow |
| start | go | quiet | fast |
| end | hurry | sound | still |

**Check-Up** Circle two words in each row that have **opposite** meanings.

| 9. | stop | look | car | go |
|---|---|---|---|---|
| 10. | door | front | back | open |
| 11. | smooth | clean | garden | dirty |
| 12. | in | out | last | next |
| 13. | left | new | quiet | right |
| 14. | below | lost | found | weak |

**Check-Up** Circle two words in each box that **sound the same,** but have different spellings and meanings.

| 15. mad   made | 16. knot   not | 17. reed   ride |
|---|---|---|
| mud   maid | note   knit | road   rode |
| 18. door   dear | 19. blew   blend | 20. tall   tail |
| deer   do | blind   blue | tell   tale |

**Check-Up** Draw a line from the word in the first column to its **synonym** in the second column.

| | | | | | |
|---|---|---|---|---|---|
| 1. begin ● | ● rush | 6. right ● | ● correct |
| 2. home ● | ● start | 7. tapped ● | ● under |
| 3. keep ● | ● house | 8. pail ● | ● sleep |
| 4. hurry ● | ● yell | 9. nap ● | ● knocked |
| 5. shout ● | ● hold | 10. below ● | ● bucket |

**Check-Up** Draw a line from the word in the first column to its **antonym** in the second column.

| | | | | | |
|---|---|---|---|---|---|
| 11. awake ● | ● fast | 16. cold ● | ● big |
| 12. close ● | ● asleep | 17. little ● | ● hot |
| 13. front ● | ● back | 18. smile ● | ● found |
| 14. alone ● | ● open | 19. moist ● | ● dry |
| 15. slow ● | ● together | 20. lost ● | ● frown |

**Check-Up** Draw a line from the word in the first column to its **homonym** in the second column.

| | | | | | |
|---|---|---|---|---|---|
| 21. eight ● | ● sales | 26. won ● | ● tide |
| 22. four ● | ● seen | 27. knew ● | ● one |
| 23. write ● | ● right | 28. tale ● | ● new |
| 24. scene ● | ● ate | 29. maid ● | ● tail |
| 25. sails ● | ● for | 30. tied ● | ● made |

**PHONICS ALIVE AT HOME** Say a word and ask your child to name a synonym. Then say another word and ask your child to name an antonym. Do the same with homonyms. Repeat the process several times.

# A WONDERFUL DAY

— 1 ✂

**Reading at Home:** After reading the book with your child, ask where the story takes place. Help your child find a word with a suffix, a word with a prefix, a synonym for **great (wonderful)**, an antonym for **full (empty)**, and a homonym for **knight (night)**.

---- Fold ----

---- Fold ----

That night, the colorful lights were like twinkling stars.

8  ✂

Then we got into an empty seat at the bottom of the Ferris wheel. As we rode to the top, we could see the cars and the road below us. This was the tallest ride I've ever been on. It was taller than my apartment building!

6

✂

read **DIRECTIONS:** Cut and fold the book.

Next we rode on an unusual roller coaster. The cars went upside down around a huge loop. I was thankful when that ride ended!

Last summer, my family went to the biggest amusement park I've ever seen. There were hundreds of families there.

First we went on the merry-go-round. The music played loudly as our horses moved up and down.

Fold — Fold

5

Name _____ Year 20____–20____

# My Progress Checklist

◯ **I need to practice this.**　　☺ **I know this.**

## Unit 1: Reviewing Consonants
◯ ☺　Consonants at the beginning of words
◯ ☺　Consonants at the end of words
◯ ☺　Consonants in the middle of words

## Unit 2: Short Vowels
◯ ☺　a
◯ ☺　i
◯ ☺　o
◯ ☺　u
◯ ☺　e

## Unit 3: Long Vowels
◯ ☺　a (a_e, ai, ay)
◯ ☺　i (i_e, ie, igh)
◯ ☺　o (o_e, oa, ow, oe)
◯ ☺　u (u_e, ui, ue)
◯ ☺　e (ee, ea)

## Unit 4: Variant Consonant Sounds and Consonant Blends
◯ ☺　Hard and soft **c**
◯ ☺　Hard and soft **g**
◯ ☺　**l** blends

◯ ☺　**r** blends
◯ ☺　**s** blends
◯ ☺　Final blends

## Unit 5: Syllables, Compound Words, y as a Vowel, Consonant Digraphs, Silent Letters, and r-Controlled Vowels
◯ ☺　Words with two syllables
◯ ☺　VCCV words
◯ ☺　VCV words
◯ ☺　Compound words
◯ ☺　Words with **y** as a vowel
◯ ☺　Words ending in **le**
◯ ☺　Silent letters in **kn, wr**

◯ ☺　Silent letters in **gn**, **mb**
◯ ☺　Initial digraphs **th, sh, wh, ch**
◯ ☺　Final digraphs **ck, th, sh, ch**
◯ ☺　**ar** words
◯ ☺　**or** words
◯ ☺　**er, ir, ur** words

## Unit 6: Vowel Digraphs and Diphthongs

| | | | | | |
|---|---|---|---|---|---|
| ○ | ☺ | **ea** | ○ | ☺ | **ou** |
| ○ | ☺ | **oo** | ○ | ☺ | **oi, oy** |
| ○ | ☺ | **au, aw** | ○ | ☺ | **ew** |
| ○ | ☺ | **ow** | | | |

## Unit 7: Contractions, Abbreviations, Plurals, and Inflectional Endings

| | | | | | |
|---|---|---|---|---|---|
| ○ | ☺ | Contractions with **not** | ○ | ☺ | Abbreviations |
| ○ | ☺ | Contractions with **will** | ○ | ☺ | Plurals with **s** |
| ○ | ☺ | Contractions with **am** | ○ | ☺ | Plurals with **es** |
| ○ | ☺ | Contractions with **is** | ○ | ☺ | Irregular plurals |
| ○ | ☺ | Contractions with **are** | ○ | ☺ | Ending **s** |
| ○ | ☺ | Contractions with **have** | ○ | ☺ | Ending **es** |
| ○ | ☺ | Contractions with **has** | ○ | ☺ | Ending **ing** |
| ○ | ☺ | Contractions with **us** | ○ | ☺ | Ending **ed** |

## Unit 8: Suffixes, Prefixes, Synonyms, Antonyms, Homonyms

| | | | | | |
|---|---|---|---|---|---|
| ○ | ☺ | Suffix **ful** | ○ | ☺ | Prefix **un** |
| ○ | ☺ | Suffix **less** | ○ | ☺ | Prefix **dis** |
| ○ | ☺ | Suffix **ness** | ○ | ☺ | Synonyms |
| ○ | ☺ | Suffix **ly** | ○ | ☺ | Antonyms |
| ○ | ☺ | Suffixes **er, est** | ○ | ☺ | Homonyms |
| ○ | ☺ | Prefix **re** | | | |